ACKNOWLEDGEMENTS

Much of the development work on the taxonomic scheme for this guide was carried out while WAW and DH were funded by Natural Environment Research Council (NERC) Studentships GT4/92/19/G and GT4/94/401/G respectively. The work also benefited greatly from grants to DJC from the British Council, the Royal Society, National Geographic Society and NERC. Thanks also to Anatoly Bobrov, Barry Warner, Janet Wilmshurst and Helen Roe for useful discussion on testate amoebae identification. We are grateful to Alan Warren of the British Museum (Natural History) for help and access to collections. Keith Barber and Frank Chambers provided useful comments on an earlier version of the manuscript. Kathrin Hörschelmann and Tanya Saiko helped with German and Russian references. Tim Absalom, of the Cartographic Resources Unit, Dept. Geographical Sciences, University of Plymouth, was responsible for the layout and redrew some of the diagrams.

CONTENTS

THE IDENTIFICATION
OF TESTATE AMOEBAE
(PROTOZOA: RHIZOPODA)
IN PEATS

Technical Guide no. 9

DAN J. CHARMAN
DAWN HENDON
WENDY A. WOODLAND

Cover illustration: *Difflugia bacillariarum* Perty 1849, a testate amoebae taxon found in bog pool habitats that uses diatom frustules to construct its test. In agglutinated taxa such as this, the outline shape of the test itself can be difficult to discern. In this case, the rim of the mouth of the test can be clearly made out on the upper left side.

Authors' addresses:

Dan J. Charman

Department of Geographical Sciences, University of Plymouth, Plymouth, Devon, PL4 8AA.

email: dcharman@plymouth.ac.uk

Dawn Hendon

School of Geography and Archaeology, University of Exeter, Exeter, EX4 4RJ.

email: dhendon@exeter.ac.uk

Wendy A Woodland

School of Geography and Environmental Management, University of the West of England, Frenchay Campus, Coldharbour Lane, Bristol, BS16 1QY.

email: Wendy3.Woodland@uwe.ac.uk

© Quaternary Research Association: London 2000

ISBN: 0 907780 48 2

ISSN: 0264 9241

Printed by: Frontier Print and Design, Pickwick House, Chosen View Road, Cheltenham, Glouc. GL51 9LT

Recommended reference:

Charman, D.J., Hendon, D. and Woodland, W.A. 2000. *The identification of testate amoebae (Protozoa: Rhizopoda) in peats.* QRA Technical Guide No. 9, Quaternary Research Association, London. 147 pp.

CHAPTER 1:
INTRODUCTION

1.1 Aims and purpose of the guide

Testate amoebae[1] (Protozoa: Rhizopoda) have been used as palaeoenvironmental indicators in peat and lake sediments for over 100 years (Lindberg, 1899, in Tolonen, 1986). Renewed interest in these organisms as palaeoenvironmental indicators has been stimulated by further ecological work (e.g. Tolonen *et al.*, 1992, 1994; Warner, 1987; Woodland *et al.*, 1998) and advances in the use of statistical techniques (Birks, 1995) for data interpretation. In the case of peatland testate amoebae, transfer functions for hydrological variables on ombrotrophic mires have been applied in Canada (Warner and Charman, 1994), the United Kingdom (Woodland *et al.*, 1998) and Switzerland (Mitchell et al., 2001), and it seems likely that similar approaches can be applied in other areas of the world (e.g. Tolonen *et al.*, 1992, 1994; Charman, 1997; Charman & Warner, 1997). However, the taxonomy of testate amoebae is still unclear and can lead to confusion in identification of sub-fossil tests (see section 1.4). A clear, reliable taxonomy, which is repeatable between observers, is required in order to develop palaeoenvironmental applications further. This is especially important to ensure comparability of data and to maximise the utility of any transfer functions based on modern training sets.

---

[1]Other terms which are sometimes used to describe the group are 'rhizopods' (e.g. Tolonen, 1986), 'arcellaceans' (e.g. Patterson *et al.,* 1985; McCarthy *et al.,* 1995) and 'thecamoebians' (e.g. Medioli and Scott, 1983).

This guide has three principal aims:

1)   To provide an identification guide suitable for new and existing researchers using testate amoebae in palaeoenvironmental work. It attempts to bring together some of the existing notes on identification already published in palaeoenvironmental literature, with older works where original species descriptions are provided.

2)   To establish a standard taxonomy for sub-fossil peatland testate amoebae which may form the basis for development. Clearly, future work will alter and adapt aspects of the taxonomy presented here, but we hope that this guide provides a baseline for this development. We appreciate that not everyone will agree with the taxa separations we present but have attempted to provide definitive and non-comparative criteria for the identification of taxa as a practical taxonomy, applicable by relative new-comers to this area of Quaternary science. Some taxa are grouped together where we have felt that separation is not consistently possible.

3)   to review the most relevant material on biology, ecology and indicator values of taxa found in peatland, principally as an aid to interpretation of fossil material.

    In meeting these aims, we hope the guide assists in the more widespread use of testate amoebae as a tool in the understanding and interpretation of fossil peat deposits. There are many potential uses of these organisms in Quaternary science but many more data need to be collected by a greater number of researchers to test this potential and to advance the techniques presented here. The guide is intended to cover all of the common taxa encountered in peat deposits in Europe and North America, but it is not comprehensive for southern hemisphere peats where there is a distinctive range of some taxa (especially *Nebela* species) in surface samples (Charman, 1997), but, to our knowledge, only a single study on fossil peats (McGlone and Wilmshurst, 1999).

The guide is divided into 6 chapters, beginning with this one which outlines the history and development of fossil testate amoebae research and introduces some of the relevant issues in the systematics and taxonomy of testate amoebae. The focus here is on the practical issues to consider in identifying fossil testate amoebae, although many of the arguments apply equally to non-fossil specimens. Chapter 2 discusses the biology and ecology of testate amoebae and their use in peatland palaeoecology, particularly the relationship between species and hydrology. Chapter 3 concerns laboratory preparation of samples and outlines some of the problems in using pollen preparation techniques for testate amoebae counts. A recommended procedure is presented, although further experimentation is encouraged too. Chapters 4 and 5 form the core of the guide, the former providing a dichotomous key for identification and the latter the full species descriptions, photographs and further notes to help in cross checking identifications based on the key. Chapter 6 reviews the indicator values of the different taxa and outlines techniques which have been used for data interpretation, including transfer function derivation and application. The final reference section is a long list of publications, including the older literature where many species were originally described. We have attempted to trace all our taxa to the original descriptions and others may also wish to do so – this section facilitates this, although we would not necessarily recommend it as much of the literature is difficult to obtain.

1.2 A brief history of testate amoebae in palaeoecology

The study of testate amoebae from fossil peats began with the work of Steinecke (1927) and Harnisch (1927), although work on lake sediments began much earlier (Lindberg, 1899 in Tolonen, 1986; Lagerheim, 1902). More recent work on fossil peats includes that of Grospietsch (1953), Frey (1964), Tolonen (1966, 1971), Tolonen *et al.* (1985), Warner and Charman (1994), Buttler *et al.* (1996), Hendon (1998), Charman *et al.* (1999) and Charman and Hendon (2000). In addition, testate amoebae have often been seen as additional indicators (Tolonen, 1986) and other peat-based studies making use of testate amoebae data combined with other information such as pollen data, include Aaby and Tauber (1975), Van Geel (1978), Barber (1981), Beyens (1984), Van der

Molen and Hoekstra (1988), Van der Molen *et al.* (1992), Dwyer and Mitchell (1997), McGlone and Wilmshurst(1999) and Mauquoy and Barber (1999). As with peatland testate amoebae, work on lake sediments has recently experienced an upsurge in interest. Initial research was largely European and was also sporadic with several papers by Schönborn (1973, 1984) and Ruzicka (1982). There have been an increasing number of papers on lake sediments published since the early 1980s, mostly in North America (Scott and Medioli, 1983; Patterson *et al.*, 1985, 1996; Patterson, 1987; Medioli and Scott, 1988; Collins *et al.*, 1990; McCarthy *et al.*, 1995; Reinhardt *et al.*, 1998; Patterson and Kumar, 2000), but also including some European work (Ellison, 1995; Asioli *et al.*, 1996).

In peatlands, testate amoebae have most commonly been used as indicators of hydrological change as they respond mainly to factors such as soil moisture and water table levels (Tolonen, 1986). While this understanding has been used subjectively for many years, recent studies have attempted to quantify the relationship between testate amoebae assemblages and fluctuations in water table and soil moisture (Charman and Warner, 1992; Tolonen *et al.*, 1992) and transfer functions have been developed for these parameters (Warner and Charman, 1994; Woodland, *et al.*, 1998; Charman, 1997; Charman and Warner, 1997; Mitchell *et al.*, 2001). Most existing work on modern assemblages and their relationship with hydrology has been based in North America (Warner, 1987; 1990; Charman and Warner, 1992, 1997; Warner and Charman, 1997) and Europe (Tolonen *et al.*, 1992, 1994; Woodland, 1996; Woodland *et al.*, 1998; Bobrov *et al.*, 1999; Mitchell *et al.*, 1999), but there is also potential for the application of similar techniques to fossil assemblages in New Zealand and the southern hemisphere peatlands (Charman, 1997; Wilmshurst, 1998; Wilmshurst and McGlone, 1999). Consequently there is now considerable interest in the use of these organisms as indicators of palaeoenvironmental change in oligotrophic peatlands. Since these are largely cosmopolitan organisms, it is likely that the identification guide can be followed in most other parts of the world, especially in the northern hemisphere, although additions and modification will be necessary for southern hemisphere peats.

1.3 Systematics

The systematics of the testate amoebae are not straightforward (Table 1). The protists are variously considered to be within the kingdom Animalia or to comprise a kingdom of their own, the Protista. The Committee on Systematics and Evolution of the Society of Protozoologists (1980) place the testate amoebae within the superclass Rhizopoda in the subphylum Sarcodina. The Rhizopoda are characterised by a possession of pseudopodia which protrude from the outer test and perform the dual functions of motility and feeding. This group also includes the Foraminifera, a large group of marine organisms. The Foraminifera however, possess complex branched pseudopodia and fall within the class Granuloreticulosea whereas the testate amoebae have simple lobe shaped or filiform pseudopodia and fall within the classes Lobosea or Filosea respectively. There is no distinct category beyond these which testate amoebae can be considered within. The orders below these classes contain many groups of organisms which do not develop outer tests and those which do contain testate species only comprise the Arcellinida (Lobosea) and Gromiida (Filosea). For most purposes, testate amoebae are therefore considered to be those species of the Lobosea and Filosea which form an outer test. This differs slightly from the earlier classification of Loeblich and Tappan (1964) where Lobosia and Filosia are considered subclasses of the classes Rhizopodea and Reticularea respectively. Tests are formed either of secreted material sometimes including regular pre-

Subkingdom	**Protozoa**
Phylum	**Sarcomastigophora** Honigberg and Balamuth 1963
Subphylum	**Sarcodina** Schmarda 1871
Superclass	**Rhizopoda** von Siebold 1845
Class	**Lobosea** Carpenter 1861
Subclass	**Testacealobosia** De Saedeleer 1934
Order	**Arcellinida** Kent 1880
Class	**Filosea** Leidy 1879a
Order	**Gromiida** Claparéde and Lachmann 1859

Table 1: Systematics of the higher taxonomy of testate amoebae based on Committee on systematics and evolution of the Society of Protozoologists (1980).

formed plates (idiosomic) or of agglutinated particles from the living environment cemented together by secretion (xenosomic). Most species have the potential to be preserved in the fossil record and in contrast to Medioli and Scott (1983) we have found good representation of both xenosomic and idiosomic tests. The structure and function of testate amoebae is described in more detail in Chapter 2.

1.4 Issues in the identification of fossil testate amoebae

Published work on the identification of testate amoebae has been based primarily on taxonomic work on modern specimens rather than fossil samples. There are several useful guides to modern specimens which are relatively accessible including Grospietsch (1958) and Corbet (1973), both of which are good starting points but they do not fully explain the rationale for separating some of the more difficult species and species groups. In addition, although they are both based mainly on test characteristics rather than details of the pseudopodia (which are decayed in fossil specimens), they do not take into account the special problems associated with techniques which aim to provide statistically significant counts of species assemblages. There are some guidelines on identification of fossil taxa from lakes in Ellison and Ogden (1987) but these are based on outline line drawings and not many of the common peatland taxa are included. Medioli and Scott (1983) also discuss taxa recovered from lake sediments and present an extremely useful and comprehensive consideration of the systematics of testate amoebae and the problems of species definitions. The alternative to using these guides is to obtain the publications where species are described for the first time or shortly afterwards. The older texts are especially useful in this respect, the volumes by Cash *et al.* (1905-1919) being particularly good together with Leidy (1879a) and Penard (1890, 1902), although several of these can be hard to obtain. Monographs and species descriptions prior to this can often be confusing as they refer to old names for many species which have subsequently been changed or even transferred to other genera. For example, Ehrenberg's work (1872) ascribes all *Euglypha* species to *Difflugia*. These publications are therefore best avoided unless there is a need to follow the origin of the taxonomy. A series of excellent monographs were published by Deflandre (1928, 1929, 1936) where most of the taxonomy is fully explained for the species considered. Some of the later monographs are also useful but often become confusing with a tendency to over-split some genera, sometimes on the basis of rather poor descriptions (eg Decloitre, 1962a, 1976, 1977a, 1977b, 1978, 1979a, 1979b, 1981, 1982; Gauthier-Lièvre and Thomas, 1958). This guide seeks to clarify some of this confusion by providing a key which encompasses most of the variation likely to be encountered in oligotrophic peats. Following a consideration of some of the main issues in the identification of fossil tests, it is concluded that more reliable identifications which can be consistently repeated between several different observers must be based on grouping of some taxa which have been split by taxonomists working on modern specimens. The rationale for this is fully explained below and throughout the rest of the guide. The taxonomy described here is designed to be a practical, comprehensive guide for those working on fossil testate amoebae from oligotrophic peatlands. The establishment of such a taxonomy is essential to building a body of comparable data in the future and to the use of transfer functions for environmental parameters such as those described by Woodland *et al.* (1998).

1.5 Taxonomic problems

The taxonomic problems which affect the identification of fossil testate amoebae from peatlands arise as a result of two main factors. Firstly, the taxonomic descriptions of extant taxa are confused; descriptions of the same species by different authors can be contradictory and apparently similar or identical specimens are given different names. This is partly a result of the particular problems associated with species definitions in uniparental organisms and is not unique to the testate amoebae (Finlay *et al.*, 1996). Secondly, there are a number of specific problems associated with the identification and counting of fossil tests in statistically significant numbers. These two aspects are further explored below to illustrate this difficulty and to provide a basis for the approach taken in the dichotomous key and taxa descriptions which follow.

Species concepts and the taxonomy of living tests

The definition of species is a fundamental prerequisite to most ecological and palaeoecological work, yet the underlying concepts are rarely considered explicitly. For organisms that reproduce sexually, divisions between species are clear in the majority of cases for living specimens and fossil material can be clearly associated with a well defined group of species even if the fossil taxon cannot be identified to species level as a result of the fossilisation process. However, for organisms that reproduce asexually, this division is not so clear as there is no unequivocal fundamental basis on which to define a species. The only alternative is to define species on the basis of morphological variation, leading to a 'morphospecies' concept (Finlay *et al.*, 1996). If this is not done, the only logical conclusion is that either all individuals are separate species or all are one species (Medioli and Scott, 1983), a practically untenable position for identification purposes. Sexual reproduction does take place in the testate amoebae (Schönborn and Peschke, 1990; Mignot and Raikov, 1992) but this is probably a relatively infrequent event and most reproduction is likely to be asexual (see section 2.2). Most reproduction is by division in which the parent constructs an entirely new test and then divides leaving one half of the nucleus and cytoplasm inside this structure. Thus, morphospecies in testate amoebae must be defined on the basis of cellular characters and the size, shape and construction of the test. However, this can lead to a wide variety of opinion on what are sufficiently distinctive morphological features for species definitions, especially since morphological plasticity can occur depending on environmental conditions (Schönborn, 1992a; Wanner and Meisterfeld, 1994). The definition of a new species is therefore a subjective judgement and opinions inevitably vary between observers. In addition to this, there are rather few biometric data for many species and new species are often described on the basis of relatively few individuals. Since morphology will often be strongly influenced by environment, unusual tests within a single sample may be a result of some unique combination of ecological factors rather than warrant the naming of a new species. Consequently, trying to identify individuals by reference to published descriptions is a fraught process simply because clear descriptions of definitive characters are hard to find and there is often little indication of the range of intra-specific morphological variation that should be accepted.

The division of phylogenetic series that are found within some genera is an issue that has been discussed by Medioli and Scott (1983) with reference to the work of Deflandre (1928). Although Deflandre suggested strongly that there were no clear distinctions between some closely related species within *Arcella*, he went on to describe a large number of species which differ in only subtle ways from one another. For this and some other genera, the picture is only further confused by later work (eg Decloitre, 1976, 1982). Medioli and Scott (1983) argue that since in many cases morphological variation is actually a continuum of change, delimitation of species along this continuum is often an arbitrary exercise. As a result of this, their nomenclature incorporates a large number of previously described species under single species. Later work by Medioli *et al.* (1987) showed that a high degree of morphological variability can be found within clonal cultures of a single species and this lends support to the arguments for grouping together very similar morphospecies. Subsequent work on the same lake-dwelling groups has shown that different morphological variants probably respond differently to environmental factors and grouped taxa have been split again and named as 'infraspecific strains'(Reinhardt *et al.*, 1998). In this guide we have attempted to separate taxa where we feel it has led to the derivation of useful palaeoenvironmental data. However, some of the separate taxa may actually be morphological variants of the same biological species. The distinction between biological species and morphospecies need not concern us further here and as far as possible we will discuss separation of 'taxa' rather than 'species'. Any identification criteria will be a compromise between practicality and possible loss of palaeoenvironmental detail. Recent ecological work on finer splitting of taxa than is presented here suggests that some taxa are divisible into several morphological variants (mainly based on size) which occupy slightly different ecological niches (Bobrov *et al.*, 1999). Further work of this nature may result in the adoption of some splitting of the taxa presented here for fossil peat studies.

Fossil testate amoebae

The problems specifically associated with the counting and identification of fossil testate amoebae can be divided into five areas:

a)   Decay of cellular contents

b)   Counting of statistically significant numbers of tests

c)   Sample preparation

d)   Changes in test morphology

e)   Morphological variability

a) Decay of cellular contents

The higher taxonomy of the sarcodines is determined by characteristics of the pseudopodia. Since the pseudopodia decays rapidly on death, these characters cannot be used in fossil or recently deceased specimens. However, divisions between taxa at lower levels are based on morphological and morphometric criteria of the test, which means that this does not present an insurmountable problem except in the separation of some taxa such as the genera *Difflugia* and *Pseudodifflugia*, which have lobose and filose pseudopodia respectively but almost identical tests in some taxa.

b) Counting of statistically significant numbers of tests

Counts of large numbers of tests are necessary to provide statistically valid assessments of the changes in species assemblages over time, in many palaeoecological studies. The high diversity and complex taphonomy of pollen means that counts are typically 3-500 but may be in excess of 1000 grains. However, for testate amoebae, counts of 150 have been shown to be representative (Warner, 1990; Woodland, 1996) in both surface and fossil samples, as diversity is lower and there are relatively few rare taxa present at any one location. Since counts may be undertaken on a large (50-200 or more) number of samples in any one study, this still represents a large amount of time by comparison with taxonomic studies which only consider a few specimens, and which may use SEM to determine test characters (e.g. Ogden and Hedley, 1980). This restricts the level of test details that can be used for identification in routine counting.

c) Sample preparation

Sample preparation for testate amoebae analysis on peats has varied between using standard pollen preparations and less chemically intensive methods (Hendon and Charman, 1997), but all samples are mounted under a coverslip on microscope slides for counting by high power (x400-1000) light microscopy. This limits ability to move tests into appropriate orientations for viewing particular features. In particular, large and/or flattened tests are difficult to rotate into lateral views. This is a particular problem in identification of *Arcella* species. Some work has been based on counting using low powered (x20-100) views of unmounted wet specimens which allows easy movement of tests, but this has only been done for the larger size fractions (>63μm) from lake and coastal sediments (e.g. Medioli and Scott, 1983; McCarthy *et al.*, 1995). This technique may underestimate the abundance and diversity of testate amoebae populations (Charman *et al.*, 1998) and since the majority of specimens present in peatlands may be smaller than 63μm, it is not an appropriate technique to use here.

d) Changes in test morphology

The degree to which the fossilisation process affects shell preservation and morphology is unknown. Assessments of preservation in mineral soils (Lousier and Parkinson, 1981) have shown differences in decay rates between species but this probably does not occur in the same way in anaerobic sediments. Distortion of tests and perhaps size changes are possible and there may be some reduction in the numbers and density of xenosomes in fossil specimens, although this is based on subjective judgements at present. As a result, identifications recommended in the literature based on the difference between round and oval cross sections (e.g. *Euglypha*, Decloitre, 1962a) should be regarded cautiously.

e) Morphological variability

It is clear from the discussion of counting techniques above that the number of specimens examined in a typical fossil study is very large in comparison to the numbers examined in the original establishment of new species. Furthermore the samples represent species variations over a large temporal scale and thus the range of variation encountered is likely to be very much greater in fossil material. Medioli and Scott (1983) suggest this is one of the major limitations in the application of modern taxonomy to fossil samples and they found that up to 75% of their specimens in lake sediments could not be classified using existing taxonomic criteria. As a result they developed a classification which could encompass more than 75% of the specimens but which grouped a large number of previously separated species. This does not seem to be such a significant problem in fossil peats where many taxa apear to morphologically rather stable. The taxa that are affected by such problems are principally from the genera *Difflugia* and *Centropyxis*.

1.6 Conclusion

Fossil testate amoebae analysis has a long history but has remained a relatively minor weapon in the arsenal of techniques available to Quaternary science. Recent developments in understanding of the ecological affinities of different taxa combined with the availability of new statistical techniques for the interpretation of data have resulted in increased interest in the use of the technique. However, the adoption of a consistent approach to the taxonomy and identification of testate amoebae is hampered by problems of species definitions in living amoebae, some confusion and poor species descriptions in the literature and problems arising from the preservation, preparation and counting of fossil specimens.

CHAPTER 2
BIOLOGY AND ECOLOGY

As testate amoebae are not well known to most Quaternary scientists, or even to many biologists, it is worth including a section describing the basic biology and functioning of these organisms here. Some aspects of the biology and structure of testate amoebae help in the explanation of patterns of spatial and temporal distribution in peats. More detailed accounts of testate amoebae biology can be found in Sleigh (1989) and Patterson and Hedley (1992). This chapter describes the basic structural elements of living testate amoebae and how they function. It also outlines the variability of test construction and factors that may affect this process, with a short discussion of reproduction and its potential implications for fossil studies. The principal factors affecting testate amoebae distribution in peatlands are also reviewed.

2.1 Structure

Figure 1 shows a living specimen of *Nebela tincta*. In its simplest division, the main elements of the living amoeba are the cell itself and the test in which it lives. The cell is composed of the nucleus and the cytoplasm that surrounds it. The cytoplasm is important in controlling the retention and loss of moisture, which is plays a large part in the response of testate amoebae to different moisture levels in peatlands. It is important that water loss is minimised during drought but that during times of excess water, the organism does not drown. Structures known as contractuole vacuoles help in this 'balancing act' by alternate swelling and collapse (Sleigh, 1989). Clearly there is a limit to the effectiveness of this process, which may differ between taxa, and could at least partly explain the observed relationship between taxa distributions and hydrological gradients.

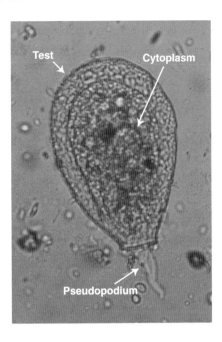

Figure 1: Living specimen of *Nebela tincta* showing the test enclosing the cytoplasm and the pseudopodium protruding through the aperture.

Part of the cytoplasm forms the pseudopodium, which is a flowing projection, extending through the pseudostome ('mouth' or aperture) of the test. It is used primarily for locomotion, attachment and feeding. As already mentioned, characteristics of the pseudopodia are used in divisions of the higher taxonomic levels within the Sarcodina, such as the distinction between the classes Lobosea (with rounded lobose pseudopodia) and Filosea (pointed or filiform pseudopodia). Likewise, some aspects of nuclei structure can be used in identification (e.g. Lüftenegger *et al.*, 1988), but since all cellular material decays rapidly on death, these features are irrelevant to identification of fossil tests. When feeding, the pseudopodium flows over and around the food particles, eventually closing and sealing the food within the cytoplasm in a food vacuole. The contents of the vacuole are digested by enzymes and absorbed into the cytoplasm. Indigestible residues can be released or in some cases may be used in construction of the test for a daughter cell (see below on reproduction, section 2.2).

The test is the outer part of the organism and, because it is preserved in sediments, it is much more important to fossil studies. The morphology, composition and size of the test determine the identity of the taxa referred to later in this guide. In living specimens, these characteristics are subordinate to those of the pseudopodia. The function of the test seems most likely to be protection from the external environment (e.g. such as drying out) and from predation. There are two basic types of test construction; autogenous (idiosomic) and xenogenous (agglutinated or xenosomic).

Autogenous tests are formed by secretion of pre-formed siliceous plates (**idiosomes**) or of a smooth proteinaceous, pseudochitinous or mucopolysaccharide material. Examples of such tests commonly found in fossil peats are those of *Assulina muscorum*, which is composed of oval siliceous plates, and *Hyalosphenia subflava*, which is formed entirely of a smooth secreted material. These tests tend to be more consistent in terms of their overall morphologies and, superficially at least, there is rather little variability between specimens. Some idiosomic taxa use plates recycled from other individuals to construct the tests. Large taxa consume smaller specimens and may retain plates and other materials for use in construction of tests for daughter cells. For example individual plates of *Euglypha* species can sometimes be observed in the tests of the genus *Nebela*.

Xenogenous or **agglutinated** tests are those constructed from the surrounding substrate and can incorporate small particles of silica, diatoms, fungal hyphae, pollen grains and other organic detritus. The nature of the agglutinated particles has been used in the separation of different species. For example, *Difflugia bacillifera* is composed of diatom frustules whereas *D. oblonga* is composed of mineral particles although it is similar in size and shape. Culturing studies show that in fact the use of particular types of xenosomes is more likely to be determined by availability of materials (Medioli *et al.*, 1987) and suggest that species definitions based on these criteria are dubious. Medioli *et al.* (1987) showed that *Difflugia tricuspis* can form autogenous daughters composed entirely of secretion when deprived of particles. Other materials such as carborundum powder could also be successfully substituted for the more usual siliceous particles. Presumably such adaptability in the use of xenosomes also exists in wild populations. However, while this is problematic for *biological* species definitions, it seems likely that different test constructions are useful to separate morphological taxa. In addition, as availability of materials used in test construction is a function of environmental conditions then these separations may be valuable when testate amoebae assemblages are used to infer environmental conditions, such as in fossil studies.

2.2 Life cycle processes

The relationships between reproduction, active tests, encystment, death and decomposition of tests are shown in Figure 2. While many elements of these processes are poorly understood quantitatively, some aspects are important to an understanding of the palaeoecology of testate amoebae, and in suggesting the advantages, problems and potential of their use as palaeoenvironmental indicators.

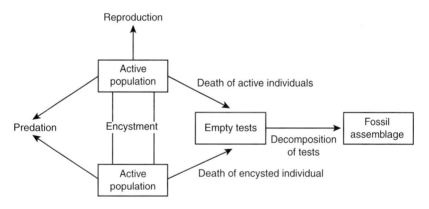

Figure 2: Main factors affecting living and dead assemblages of testate amoebae (adapted from Lousier and Parkinson, 1981).

Reproduction

Testate amoebae mostly reproduce by asexual binary fission. However, there have been two studies that suggest that sexual reproduction occurs occasionally. Schönborn and Peschke (1990) observed what appeared to be sexual reproduction in clonal cultures of *Assulina*. In the ninth month of a 15 month study, one occurrence of copulation was observed, the two parental organisms uniting with their pseudostomes and forming a third test, into which the cytoplasm of both parents flowed. The nuclei fused and the cytoplasm secreted a cyst wall. Mignot and Raikov (1992) observed meiosis from electron microscopy studies of *Arcella vulgaris* and concluded that testate amoebae can no longer be considered to be entirely asexual. Despite the fact that sexual reproduction clearly does occur from time to time, and therefore in theory biological species concepts could be applied in the taxonomy of testate amoebae, this would be unworkable in practice.

Rates of reproduction are rather poorly known but from laboratory and field observations, Heal (1964) suggested that there are less than ten generations of testate amoebae per annum, depending on the species. Schönborn (1992b) recorded between 9-27 generations per annum in mosses, but was not able to conclude whether this was representative or not. Small species such as *Assulina muscorum* have a higher turnover than larger tests such as *Nebela collaris*. Other studies suggest population doubling times of only a few days (Ogden, 1981; Lousier, 1984a, 1984b). Seasonal variability of reproduction rates is also poorly known but some data suggest there are seasonal variations with fastest doubling times in spring (Lousier, 1984a, 1984b). Clearly reproduction is a relatively fast process and in theory this should make testate amoebae temporally sensitive indicators of palaeoenvironmental changes in peats and other sediments. It is also possible that testate amoebae assemblages are more strongly related to some aspect of seasonal conditions rather than mean annual conditions. However, research in this area has not been undertaken to date.

Encystment

Encystment is a survival mechanism for inhospitable environments, whereby the organism seals the aperture with a plug and the volume of the cytoplasm contracts by dehydration. The cyst is capable of withstanding desiccation, freezing and lack of food. This has two implications for fossil studies. Firstly, it means that faunas will not be unduly affected by short term fluctuations in environmental conditions and is thus an advantage in their use as palaeoenvironmental indicators (Medioli *et al.*, 1990). Secondly, it means they may not be as sensitive to environmental change as reproduction rates suggest. However, as a single sample of fossil peat straddles a period of at least several years of life and death of testate amoebae communities, the effect of these shorter term processes may be negligible (Meisterfeld, 1977). Rates of encystment and survival times are largely unknown so the actual implications of this process for fossil studies are purely speculative.

Test decomposition

The possibility of decomposition of tests is an important issue for fossil studies. Individual tests are generally rather well preserved in peats and partial tests or test frag-ments are not often found. However, Lousier and Parkinson (1981) found evidence of differential test decay in forest soils (Table 2). They suggested that xenogenous tests with robust cement layers and chitinous idiosomic tests were less susceptible to decay than idiosomic tests. Some support for this pattern of resistance to decay can be found in fossil peat assemblages. For example, *Arcella* and *Amphitrema flavum* are common taxa in many fossil assemblages and both are composed of a chitinous secretion. *Difflugia*, *Centropyxis* and *Cyclopyxis* are also common and could be categorised as robust xenogenous tests. However, *Hyalosphenia subflava* is one of the commonest taxa in highly decayed fossil peats, yet it is in Lousier and Parkinson's 'least resistant' category, being composed of secretion. Likewise *Assulina muscorum* is an idiosomic test con-structed of oval siliceous plates, yet it is also abundant in fossil peats, and even fre-quently survives pollen preparation treatments (see Chapter 3). Thus while post-mortem decay of a fraction of the fauna is possible, there is no clear and consistent evidence of whether this has differential effect on taxa.

Dispersal

Living and encysted tests can be transported on birds' feet and possibly in their faeces, which may explain the cosmopolitan distribution of many taxa. In addition, the encysted tests could be moved by wind during dry periods. While this may have an influence on the major biogeographic distributions of tests, it seems unlikely to affect local distribution to any great extent, especially on peatlands where the surface is very wet for the major part of the year. Small scale spatial variability of testate amoebae faunas on patterned peatlands also suggests that lateral displacement of tests is limited (e.g. Tolonen *et al.*, 1992). The degree of downwashing of dead amoebae in the upper peats is unknown but is likely to be similar to that of pollen grains, since the size range of tests is similar. Tolonen (1986) suggests this does not have a significant influence on the necrocoenoses.

2.3 Ecology

The most important factor affecting species distributions on peatlands is undoubtedly moisture availability and this is discussed at length in the next section. However, other factors affect testate amoebae and some of these have a bearing on the use and interpretation of fossil assemblages.

	Taxon	**Test construction**
Most resistant	*Arcella* spp.	Chitinous
	Most *Difflugia* spp. *Phryganella acropodia* *Cyclopyxis eurystoma* *Centropyxis aerophila*	Sediment particles embedded in robust layers of cement
	Euglypha spp. *Trinema lineare* *Difflugia oviformis*	Platelets
Least resistant	*Hyalosphenia subflava* *Heleopera petricola*	Secretion

Table 2: Relative resistance to decay for empty testate amoebae shells according to Lousier and Parkinson (1981).

Food availability

There are limits to the size of food which testate amoebae can consume as most taxa are limited to prey that is smaller in diameter than their pseudostome. The pseudopodia withdraw inside the test carrying bacteria, fungi, algae and even other protozoa. Figure 3 shows a *Placocista spinosa* consuming an *Amphitrema flavum*, just large enough to fit within its pseudostome. However, there are exceptions to this as observed by Heal (1964) who recorded a *Difflugia tuberculata* that consumed a large desmid (*Closterium*) larger than its pseudostome. Using the pseudopodia, the amoebae snapped the desmid in half and inserted the pseudopodia inside the cell to remove the algae. Heal (1964) estimated that testate amoebae in cultures can consume their own volume in food each day. In addition, some taxa have zoochlorellae (e.g. *Amphitrema wrightianum*), which they use for photosynthesis and these species may not need to rely on consumption of other organisms.

Clearly though, the amount of food available will have some effect on the testate amoebae fauna. In peatlands, the availability of food may be related to moisture conditions, for example as algae decrease in abundance across a pool to hummock succession, with increasingly dry conditions. Any autocorrelation with moisture makes it difficult to separate effects of food availability and hydrology in field based ecological studies. In reproduction, frequency of division increases with greater abundance of food, but if a certain threshold of food concentration is exceeded, the frequency of division may actually decrease (Schönborn, 1992b). Food availability (combined with temperature) can also cause significant changes in shell and pseudostome diameter in clonal cultures of *Trinema lineare* and *Cyclopyxis kahli* (Wanner and Meisterfeld, 1994). This may be related to the fact that the size of the amoeba is controlled by the volume of cytoplasm available in the parent test at the time of division (Medioli *et al.,* 1990). In turn cytoplasm volume in the parent is likely to be affected by the quantity of food available.

Temperature, light and oxygen

Within a single mire, temperature, light and oxygen levels are likely to be closely related. Temperature fluctuations are greatest at the surface and light and oxygen levels

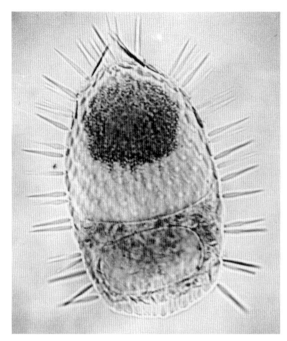

Figure 3: *Placocista spinosa* Carter 1865 consuming a test of *Amphitrema flavum* Archer 1877. Photograph from a slide from the Penard Collection at the British Museum (Natural History).

both decrease with depth in the acrotelm (the upper aerated zone, see Ingram, 1978). While higher temperatures appear to decrease generation times (Schönborn, 1962b), it seems unlikely that this will affect assemblages in a particular location to a significant extent. However, light and oxygen are important in determining the vertical living space of testate amoebae, especially within *Sphagnum* communities. The capitula of the *Sphagnum* plants intercept most of the light reaching the surface but there is enough light in the upper few centimetres for photosynthesis by some species that possess symbiotic zoochlorellae. Thus species such as *Hyalosphenia papilio*, *Placocista spinosa*, *Amphitrema flavum* and *A. wrightianum* may be limited by the availability of light (Meisterfeld, 1977). Likewise as levels of free oxygen decrease with depth, there are few living tests (Corbet, 1973). Changes in light and oxygen therefore result in a vertical zonation of testate amoebae in the fresh *Sphagnum* at the surface of a peatland (Heal, 1962; Schönborn, 1963; Meisterfeld, 1977). Changes in the vertical distribution of testate amoebae are important when obtaining surface samples for modern data sets (e.g. Woodland *et al.*, 1998) as well as when studying fossil assemblages in upper peats. The zone of living amoebae is probably highly variable depending on the surface vegetation and especially on the bulk density of the topmost part of the profile and it is therefore difficult to give precise guidelines. However, for surface samples to be used in modern training sets, a maximum of the upper 5-6cm is likely to be representative unless the acrotelm is very deep and the surface moss very loose (as for example in the *Sphagnum recurvum* studied by Heal, 1962).

It is usually recommended that the top green capitula are not included in the sample (Warner, 1987; Tolonen *et al.*, 1992). This is because it is thought that the moss immediately below the surface is more likely to be representative of the necrocoenosis. Conversely, some *Sphagnum* is more compact and provides a much denser substrate in which case the living zone may only be 2-3cm deep. More studies on different substrates are required to discover further details of these differences. For fossil studies that use upper peats, fossil assemblages are unlikely to be affected by the living community except in the upper 10cm or less. Further work attempting to separate living and dead amoebae in upper peats is underway to elucidate this issue further (Charman and Hendon, unpublished).

Water chemistry

Various aspects of peatland water chemistry have been linked to variations in testate amoebae assemblage but all appear to be less important than the amount of water present. pH is probably the most important and most widely studied aspect of water chemistry affecting the distribution of testate amoebae on peatlands, but since it is often related to other parameters it may simply be a surrogate for one, or more likely, a combination of these factors. Most studies report some relationship with pH (e.g. Heal, 1961) and in multivariate analyses it is generally found to be the second most important variable related to assemblage composition after surface wetness variables (Tolonen *et al.*, 1994; Charman and Warner, 1992, 1997). Only when very narrow pH ranges are sampled does pH appear to be of minor importance, such as on ombrotrophic and oligotrophic mires (Woodland, 1996). Other variables may also be important and dissolved organic carbon concentrations and C:N ratios have some influence, albeit a relatively minor one

(Tolonen, 1986; Tolonen *et al.*,1992, 1994). Water chemistry is much more important in lake-dwelling faunas (Tolonen, 1986; Costan and Planas, 1986). Although there are rather few data from fen peats, it is possible that testate amoebae could be a useful indicator of past changes in acidity on mires.

Hydrology

The relationship between hydrology and species occurrence is the principal reason for most studies of fossil testate amoebae on peatlands. The importance of hydrology in controlling the occurrence and relative abundance of different taxa has been well known for a number of years but there have been a series of developments in describing and understanding this relationship. The principal reason for this relationship is that the water film on the host substrate is the living space for the amoebae. Flattened tests and small size both enable amoebae to inhabit and move within very small water filled spaces and adaptations such as cryptostomy and plagiostomy (modification to the size and orientation of the aperture) help prevent desiccation.

Harnisch (1927) began ecological work on peatlands by describing four species associations relating to different types of mire which, in hindsight, can be seen to actually be a hydrological series. De Graaf (1956) also classified taxa hydrologically into hydrophilous (inhabiting submerged mosses), hygrophilous (in moist conditions) and xerophilous (dry conditions) categories with a fourth eurytopic group apparently showing no clear preference. De Graaf (1956) used essentially the same categories but split the hydrophiles into two categories (α-hydrophilous and ß-hydrophilous) . The terminology was highly subjective until Schönborn (1962) matched testate amoebae assemblages to Jung's (1936) eight hydrological categories for peatlands. This was further improved by the semi-quantitative scale of Meisterfeld (1977) who attached estimated % moisture values to Jung's categories, as well as providing suggestions for field assessments based on the amount of water squeezed from surface mosses with 'weak', 'moderate' or 'strong' pressure (Table 3).

Further advances came with properly quantified soil moisture measurements related to testate amoebae communities (Tolonen *et al.*, 1985; Warner, 1987, 1989). In these studies, soil moisture was measured gravimetrically in the same samples that were used for testate amoebae counts. Thus more precise estimates of soil moisture preferences were obtained for individual taxa. Further work in the 1990s followed this principle but has also examined relationships with other environmental parameters, including other hydrological variables such as depth to water table and influence of mire water pH

Testate amoebae group (de Graaf, 1956)	Moisture class (Jung, 1936)	Relative water content (Jung, 1936)	Moisture content (Meisterfeld,1977)
	I	Open water or submerged vegetation	>95%
Hygrophilous	II	Floating vegetation, partly submerged, partly at the surface	>95%
	III	Emerged vegetation, very wet, water drops out without pressure	>95%
α-hydrophilous	IV	Wet, water drops out with moderate pressure	~95%
	V	Half-wet, water drops out with moderate pressure	85-95%
β-hydrophilous	VI	Moist, water drops out with strong pressure	85-90%
Xerophilous	VII	Half-dry, a few drops with strong pressure	<80%
	VIII	Dry, no water drops with strong pressure	<50%

Table 3: Classification of wetness values for habitats of peatland-dwelling testate amoebae according to Jung (1936) and Meisterfeld (1977) and compiled by Tolonen (1986). Many subsequent papers referred these moisture classes when discussing habitat preferences of specific taxa.

and other water quality variables (Tolonen *et al.*, 1992, 1994; Warner and Charman, 1994; Charman and Warner, 1992, 1997; Woodland *et al.*, 1998; Bobrov *et al.*, 1999; Mitchell *et al.*, 1999). All of these studies confirm that hydrology is the most important influence on testate amoebae assemblages, whether it is measured as soil moisture or depth to water table (Figure 4).

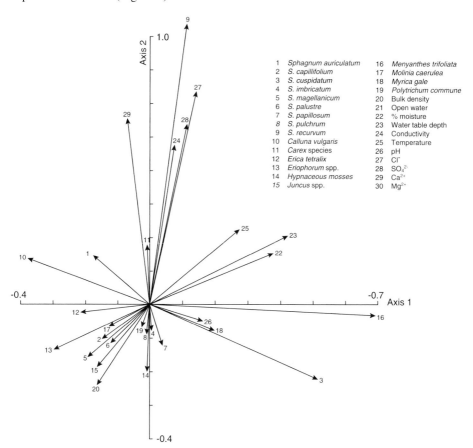

Figure 4: The relative importance of different environmental variables for the composition of testate amoebae assemblages as shown by a Canonical Correspondence Analysis of a data set from Britain. The length of the arrows indicates the strength of the relationship with species assemblages and the direction shows whether the variable is related to the primary axis (one) or the secondary axis (two). Adapted from Woodland *et al.* (1998). The abundance (in %) of host species of plants are also included here as variables which could influence the distribution of testate amoebae but they are also autocorrelated with the hydrological and water chemistry variables.

The remaining problem with these improved data sets is that it is still rather difficult to compare between studies due to soil moisture levels being made at only a single point in time. In most cases, logistic constraints prevent repeat measurements of soil moisture or water table depth. While internally comparable data can be obtained by restricting sampling to a short time interval, these data are not usually comparable to other data collected during another year or season. Charman and Warner (1992) suggested the use of ranked hydrological preferences and made some comparisons between Finland and continental Canada (Table 4). While mean absolute values are much lower for the Canadian data set, the rankings demonstrate that many taxa occur in the same hydrological niche over very wide geographic areas. To date, geographical comparisons have been limited by the difficulty with comparability of data but further work is possible even based on existing data. Given the highly cosmopolitan distribution of many taxa, it would be interesting to know if they occupy similar niches in widely separated regions.

One way of overcoming the comparability of data is to base the calculations for the hydrological optimum for each taxon on mean annual data. Unfortunately this is not always possible, but by utilising existing long-term water table monitoring sites, some progress has been made in this direction. Tolonen *et al.* (1992) used one site where these data were available but so far only Britain has a significant amount of data relating testate amoebae to mean annual water tables (Woodland, 1996; Woodland *et al.*, 1998). Further data of this kind are important to the development of understanding testate amoebae responses to different water table conditions.

Hydrology has also been shown to affect the size of individuals within a particular taxon. Heal (1963) observed that larger testate amoebae were associated with wetter moss, probably due to the larger space available in the thicker water film. Bobrov *et al.* (1999) also demonstrate that in general larger taxa within a closely related group, occupy wetter locations than the smaller taxa. In a palaeoecological study, it is possible to test this theory by assessing whether periods with low reconstructed water tables were composed of small fraction taxa and conversely whether larger taxa dominate the assemblage at the points where the water table was high. Recording the sizes of individuals and their changing ratios over time may yield useful information on past wetness levels, although to our knowledge this has not yet been attempted.

Taxon	NE Ontario		Finland	
	%	Rank	%	Rank
Hyalosphenia papilio	88.80	1	95.1	5
Amphitrema flavum	86.27	2	96.0	1
Hyalosphenia elegans	83.90	3	95.3	4
Centropyxis aculeata	78.54	4	95.6	2
Heleopera sphagni	78.02	5	94.1	8
Hyalosphenia ovalis	77.06	6	94.5	7
Euglypha tuberculata	74.38	7	90.0	11
Euglypha rotunda	71.03	8	89.6	12
Assulina seminulum	70.40	9	92.2	9
Corythion spp.	70.17	10	87.0	15
Heleopera petricola	70.12	11	95.6	2
Nebela militaris	69.95	12	89.3	13
Assulina muscorum	68.66	13	86.6	17
Euglypha strigosa	68.15	14	94.8	6
Arcella artrocrea	67.53	15	87.4	14
Bullinularia indica	67.50	16	80.9	22
Trigonopyxis arcula	67.43	17	85.1	18
Centropyxis aerophila	67.29	18	83.6	20
Nebela parvula	64.55	19	86.7	16
Nebela tincta	64.08	20	83.2	21
Cyclopyxis arcelloides	63.66	21	84.1	19
Arcella catinus	44.18	22	91.7	10

Table 4: Ranked hydrological preferences and absolute values as weighted averages of abundant taxa common to two studies in Finland (Tolonen *et al.*, 1992) and northeast Ontario, Canada (Charman and Warner, 1992). Comparisons are based on moisture content of the substrate at the time of sampling. While absolute values are difficult to compare between studies due to difference in sampling conditions for hydrological variables, ranking provides an indication of the comparability of habitat preferences between different geographical regions. Taxa which are not common to both sites are excluded from the table.

CHAPTER 3
SAMPLE PREPARATION AND LABORATORY TECHNIQUES

3.1 Sample preparation and potential problems

Despite, or perhaps because of, the variety of studies in which testate amoebae have been used (see Chapter 1), there have been a number of different methods used in sample preparation. Tolonen (1986) and Warner (1990) provide the closest to standard procedures for peats, and Hendon and Charman (1997) have developed these further. The techniques which have been used fall into two groups. Firstly there are preparations which are based on pollen preparation methods using a variety of chemical pretreatments to eliminate unwanted detritus. Secondly, there are those which are undertaken specifi-cally for testate amoebae analysis and which are generally based on a combination of dispersal in water and sieving. Pollen type preparations are clearly more efficient in terms of time, since pollen and other microfossils can be counted at the same time. How-ever, it has been known for some time that these techniques are likely to lead to a loss of some testate amoebae due to the tests being more fragile than the much more resistant pollen grains. Recent work has shown experimentally that some pollen-based approaches are highly destructive and result in a loss of diversity and abundance of the testacean fauna (Hendon and Charman, 1997). The following section explores the different ap-proaches used, highlights a currently recommended preparation technique and discusses other possible further developments for particular kinds of sample. In discussing impacts of different preparations, we draw heavily on Hendon and Charman (1997).

3.2 Impacts of different procedures

Procedures described by Tolonen (1966, 1986) modified the method of Grospietsch (1953, 1958) and variants of this have been widely used in the preparation of modern samples (Tolonen *et al.*, 1992, 1994; Warner, 1987, 1990). The technique is simple; disaggregation in boiling water followed by sieving at 750μm to remove larger debris before mounting on slides beneath a coverslip. Smaller mesh sizes (300μm) have been found to reduce the amount of debris considerably (Woodland, 1996) and there are almost no tests larger than this in peatlands. Techniques for lake sediments have differed from these with examination of the fraction *retained* on a 45 or 63μm sieve (e.g. Medioli and Scott, 1983; Reinhardt *et al.*, 1998) and examination in open trays using high powered dissecting microscopes. Although this may be appropriate where only larger taxa are likely to be encountered, on peatlands there are many smaller taxa which are important components of the overall assemblage. In saltmarshes, the larger size fraction is only a small proportion of the total assemblage (Charman *et al.*, 1998). However, the amount of unwanted debris on slides can make counting difficult and anything that can be done to reduce this is worth exploring. We have found it beneficial to use a microsieve (15μm) to remove unwanted fine debris from many fossil samples. Chemical treatments are potentially an attractive option and as mentioned above many past studies have used this approach particularly where other microfossils are also being examined. Hendon and Charman (1997) therefore assessed the impacts of different chemical treatments on the composition of testate amoebae samples from an ombrotrophic peat to assess the impacts of these treatments on results obtained.

In this study, five replicates of each of six subsamples were subjected to a different preparation procedures (Table 5), reflecting the range of preparation treatments used in published work and potential techniques which would exploit some of the advantages of pollen preparation while avoiding more damaging procedures. All samples were prepared with 1cm³ peat and one *Lycopodium* tablet (Stockmarr, 1971) to calculate concentrations, mounted in glycerol and counted at x400 magnification. For each sample, 200 *Lycopodium* spores were counted. Raw count data are presented in Table 6 and percentage data are shown in Figure 5. The raw count data are equivalent to concentration data as the same number of *Lycopodium* spores were counted in each sample. The rotifer *Habrotrocha angusticollis* was also included in the count.

Treatment	A	B	C	D	E
Boiling water (10 mins)	+	-	-	-	-
10% NaOH (10 mins)	-	+	-	+	-
10% KOH (10 mins)	-	-	+	-	+
Acetylation (10 mins)	-	+	-	-	-
Acetylation (3 mins)	-	-	+	+	-
Sieve (300μm)	+	-	+	-	+
Sieve (180μm)	-	+	-	+	-
Micro sieve (15μm)	+	-	-	-	-

Table 5: Summary of treatments for sample preparation used by Hendon and Charman (1997). + indicates treatment carried out. Preparation A is modified from Tolonen (1986), preparations B - D are variations of procedures for pollen analysis, preparation E is a simple alkaline digestion.

Pollen preparations

Preparations B, C and D are standard pollen preparations (Moore *et al.*, 1991), with variations in alkali treatment and acetylation periods. Preparation B also includes a 300μm sieve rather than the standard 180μm sieve used in pollen preparation to see if additional tests were recovered. In all three pollen preparation experiments, only approximately one fifth of the potential tests were recovered, when compared to the testate amoebae preparation (A). An acetylation time of ten minutes is slightly more destructive than a three minute acetylation, but a significant number of tests and half the potential diversity of species are still destroyed even with this less harsh treatment. The use of different alkalis for deflocculation (NaOH or KOH) does not affect results and the larger sieve size yields similar numbers of tests. However, the latter result only applied to this particular peat type and it may be dangerous to assume that smaller sieve sizes could be

Table 2: Raw count data for preparations A-E.

Species	Preparation A						Preparation B						Preparation C						Preparation D						Preparation E					
	1	2	3	4	5	6	1	2	3	4	5	6	1	2	3	4	5	6	1	2	3	4	5	6	1	2	3	4	5	6
Amphitrema flavum	23	40	29	20	13	5	4	10	5	2	3		2	2	5	10	5		4	3	5	7	6	1	76	70	41	31	5	6
Amphitrema wrightianum	44	35	3	4	2																				32	14	2			2
Arcella discoides type			1	2	1	5		1	5	2	13		1		12	4	10	1			7	2	1	1		1		13	7	4
Arcella gibbosa type	2	1	2	2	1																							1		
Assulina muscorum	8	61	18	13	4		13	18	10	19	6	3	26	23	5	17	4		13	26	11	16	11	6	10	146	67	21	2	
Assulina seminulum		3	7				1													4	2	2		1		6	14	4		
Cryptodifflugia sacculus	1	3	116	82	86	41	1													2	1				1	2	537	295	86	29
Centropyxis arcelloides type	5	12	25	13	9	7	1						1	2	1												24	11	4	
Difflugia pristis type	6	13	17	15	9	1												3							4	39	70	69	24	28
Euglypha rotunda type	1																													
Heleopera petricola	3	2																									10	3	1	
Hyalosphenia subflava			22	9	3	2							2	3		1			3	8	4		1	2			29	10	10	2
Nebela flabellulum	2	1																												
c.f. *Phryganella acropodia*				1																										
Habrotrocha angusticollis	29	1			2	1										2	1		8			1			59	7		1	1	1
Centropyxis aculeata type																										1				
Amphitrema stenostoma																									6	27		3		
Bullinularia indica																										8				1
Trigonopyxis arcula type																														1
Total	124	172	241	160	131	62	21	32	21	24	22	3	32	30	23	36	22	6	33	41	28	28	19	11	189	322	794	462	140	68

Table 6: Table 2: Raw count data for preparations A-E (modified from Hendon and Charman, 1997). The taxa are identified to species level except where named as a 'type', when more than one species may be represented. *Habrotrocha angusticollis* is a rotifer. Details of preparations included in the text but abbreviated versions as follows. A: modified Tolonen (1986), B: NaOH + 10 minute acetylation + 180μm sieve, C: KOH + 3 minute acetylation + 300μm sieve, D: NaOH + 3 minute acetylation + 180μm sieve, E: simple KOH digestion + 300μm sieve.

used universally. Different species are affected to different degrees (see figure 5). All treatments show a loss or large reduction in the species *Difflugia pristis* type, *Euglypha rotunda* type, *Heleopera petricola*, *Nebela flabulellum* and *Cyclopyxis arcelloides* type. The loss of *Difflugia pristis* type is especially severe as it is present consistently and in high concentrations in preparations A and E. The contrast between preparations E and B-D confirms that acetylation is the most damaging treatment and may particularly affect agglutinated taxa such as *D. pristis* type.

Other taxa are not lost completely but are reduced in concentration, even when they were originally present in quite large numbers (e.g. *Amphitrema flavum*). Of course, relative abundances (figure 5) are strongly skewed by the combined effects of test destruction and concentration reductions. Surviving taxa are over-represented (*Arcella discoides* type, *Amphitrema flavum* and *Assulina muscorum*) and some trends in the diagram are changed. For example, an increasing curve in *A. flavum* (Preparation A) appears as a reducing curve in preparations B-D. Although total counts are low, the results suggest that testate amoebae data from such pollen preparation procedures are unlikely to be reliable.

Water-based and alkali digestion techniques

Preparation A is a modification of Tolonen (1986) with a smaller sieve size to remove more of the larger debris (300μm) and the addition of a micro-sieve (15μm) to remove fine detritus to improve slide clarity. Preparation E is a simple KOH digestion. Since KOH alone can produce reasonable pollen slides from certain peats (Moore *et al.*, 1991), it was thought that this technique could provide a suitable treatment for combined pollen and testate amoebae analysis.

The results from preparations A and E are comparable in many respects and based on the concentrations and total number of taxa recorded are clearly superior to pollen based techniques in terms of the quality of the record. However, there are a number of important and surprising differences between the two procedures. The species assemblage of both sets of preparations are similar, although four species present in prepara-

Figure 5: Testate amoebae percentage diagrams from five preparations A-E (Hendon and Charman, 1997 - see Table 5). A: modified Tolonen (1986), B: NaOH + 10 minute acetylation + 180μm sieve, C: KOH + 3 minute acetylation + 300μm sieve, D: NaOH + 3 minute acetylation + 180μm sieve, E: simple KOH digestion + 300μm sieve.

tion E are absent from preparation A, and three species present in preparation A are absent from preparation E. However, these are all taxa which have very low counts (<3% of total) and these differences are probably an artefact of the count totals used. The patterns of change in the percentage diagrams are almost identical, with the exception of a larger count of *Difflugia pristis* type in the basal sample of preparation E. This appears anomalous with the rest of the results and could be due to a real difference in the samples as biostratigraphic change may not be exactly horizontal in the core. The most striking difference between the preparations is that concentrations in E are almost twice those of A. This is perplexing as preparation A is theoretically the least damaging of the procedures. The most likely explanation is that KOH treatment disperses the sediment more effectively than disaggregation in boiling water. As a result a significant amount of tests are retained on the 300μm sieve reducing the overall concentration counted in preparation A. From comparison with the KOH treatment, this does not appear to affect taxa differentially. Both procedures appear to yield good quality data but the counting of treatment E was hampered by poor test preservation. Tests appeared damaged and many features were altered or removed. In this case, this did not result in a total impediment to identification but this could occur in some species assemblages where identification is more difficult. In addition, where original preservation is poor, further damage may make identification impossible.

3.3 Recommended preparation and long term curation

The preparation experiment, carried out by Hendon and Charman (1997) show that both the concentration and number of testate amoebae taxa recorded in samples subjected to conventional pollen analysis will be severely reduced. This affects concentration and relative abundance data. As much as 80% of the potential assemblage is destroyed by pollen treatments. The variable impact of pollen treatments might go some way to explaining the varying views on the utility of testate amoebae analysis in previous studies. Aaby (1976) found that testate amoebae results matched inferences from humification analyses yet others found that there was little to be gained from them (e.g. Barber, 1981). The two species most commonly found in pollen studies are *Amphitrema flavum* and *Assulina* spp. which may be due either to their resistance to chemical treatment, or it may be because these species are relatively easy to identify. The comparisons of treatments show that it cannot be assumed that all specimens of any species are adequately preserved for even relative abundance trends to be used as palaeoenvironmental evidence – they may simply result from slight differences in treatment times or perhaps even in peat types. Although alkali treatment alone worked well in terms of final results, the process was hindered by damage to tests and it cannot be assumed that it will work adequately in all peat types. Thus the conclusion of Hendon and Charman (1997) was that water-based sieving techniques are the only appropriate preparation technique for testate amoebae in peats. Sieve size is a matter of judgement – clearly the aim is to eliminate as much of the debris as possible without actually removing any of the testate amoebae. In general, the 15-300μm fraction provides a good safety margin but some work with smaller upper sieve sizes (180 and even 125μm) suggests it may be possible to reduce this a little in some circumstances. Microsieving can take a little more time but this is more than compensated for by the reduced counting times. The following procedure is therefore recommended for most circumstances. It is modified from Tolonen (1986),Warner (1990) and Hendon and Charman (1997).

1. Subsample peat core and place a known volume (normally 2cm^3 is adequate) in a 250ml beaker.
2. Add one tablet of the innoculum *Lycopodium clavatum* L. (Stockmarr,1971) as an exotic marker to give quantitative rhizopod analysis. These may be dissolved in dilute HCl, and rinsed in distilled water before adding.
3. Boil in 100 ml distilled water for 10 minutes and stir occasionally with glass rods to disaggregate the peat. The boiling merely serves as a mechanical disaggregation and may not always be necessary. Prolonged soaking (4 hours to overnight) also helps this process.
4. Wash each sample through a coarse sieve (300μm mesh) to remove the coarse detritus, and back-sieve through 15μm mesh to remove the fine fraction detritus with distilled water. Retain material between 15μm and 300μm.
5. Wash the remains of each sample into centrifuge tubes and, if there is much excess water, centrifuge at 3000 rpm for five minutes.
6. Pour off supernatant. Staining can be carried out (as recommended by most

authors) but this does not always result in improvements and can be omitted. If staining is required, add two drops of safranine to the concentrate and wash twice with distilled water.

7. Samples can be stored with a small amount of distilled water and ethanol in stoppered vials. We have previously used glycerol as a storage medium and mountant (Hendon and Charman, 1997) but have found two problems with this. Firstly, the optical quality of slides is reduced and secondly, it is difficult to use specimens for SEM work once they have been in contact with glycerol.

8. For mounting, samples can be counted in water only or using an aqueous mountant such as glycerol, Canada balsam or glycerol jelly. We tend to use plain water mounts but slides have to be counted quickly before they dry out and cannot be archived. More work needs to be done on finding suitable mountants to avoid this problem without reducing optical quality and manoeuvrability of the specimens. Glycerol jelly is ideal for long term storage but it is not so easy to manoeuvre specimens during counting.

Possible developments

As more peat types are examined and as greater effort is put into obtaining countable numbers of testate amoebae from 'difficult' samples it may be possible to develop further the basic approach outlined above. Several possibilities have been hinted at; use of different sieve sizes, alternative mountants, possibly even more limited chemical treatment may be worth trying. Gravity separation is another possibility which has been suggested (R. Scaife pers. comm.). Few of these approaches have been properly trialled yet but any that are should be carefully evaluated before use if comprehensive and comparable assessments of testate amoebae assemblages are to be obtained from peat samples.

CHAPTER 4
A DICHOTOMOUS KEY

Due to the considerable problems with the interpretation and application of the existing taxonomic descriptions to fossil material from peatlands, the following key and descriptions with taxonomic notes have been devised to provide clear and unequivocal guidance on identification in future studies. The most critical aspect of this guide is to clearly differentiate between the taxa that we have adopted in our studies to date. This is particularly important in separating taxa that appear to be part of a continuum of change in size and/or shape. While some divisions based on existing indications in the literature probably remain somewhat arbitrary, these divisions may still remain valuable in the use of testate amoebae as palaeoenvironmental indicators. Our primary concern has been to provide guidelines that can consistently be applied between researchers at the lowest taxonomic level. Only subsequent work will show whether some of the divisions really are separating morphospecies with distinctly different ecological requirements or not. If this is not the case, then clearly there is an argument for further grouping of the taxa we describe here. Equally, there may be an argument for further division of some taxa when the orientation of particular specimens makes this possible. However, unless this can be consistently achieved for all similar specimens it is probably not worthwhile and may result in spurious conclusions on diversity and differences between assemblages.

Some key terms used in dichotomous key and species descriptions

The terminology used here has been kept as simple as possible, but there are some terms which are not in common use and others which have been used in a variable sense.

Definitions of the main terms used here are based on Corbet (1973).

Shape of test

elongate	test length >1.5x test breadth.
spherical	test is close to, or perfectly, circular.
ovoid	test is oval-shaped, with convex sides.
pyriform	test is pear-shaped, wider at the posterior end than the anterior.

The aperture (also referred to as pseudostome or mouth)

terminal	aperture situated at the end of the test, at right angles to the long axis of the test.
subterminal	aperture at or near one end of the test but not symmetrically at right angles to the long axis (as in *Trinema* and *Corythion*).

Test orientation and regions

broad lateral view	Seen from the broadest side of the test with the pseudostome uppermost.
narrow lateral view	Seen from the narrowest side of the test with the pseudostome uppermost.
pole	situated at both ends of the long axis of the test.
apertural	in broad lateral view, the region of the test surrounding the aperture. Also referred to as the anterior region.
aboral	in broad lateral view, the region of the test farthest from the aperture. Also referred to as the posterior region.

Other features

collar	short (<10µm) extension surrounding the test aperture.
neck	extension from test, terminated by an aperture.
lateral pores	pores at the test margins in broad lateral view.

The key

The key can be used to determine the identity of most of the taxa that are encountered in oligotrophic peatlands in northwest Europe and North America. Some taxa are included which we have not encountered but which have been reported in other studies. Detailed descriptions and photographs are not included for these taxa but they included in the key for the sake of completeness and are identified with a *. There are some groups (Difflugiidae in particular) where we would expect that other taxa may be encountered, but these should be limited to the more mesotrophic sites. Determinations should be cross checked with the photographs and descriptions before positive identifications are made. In addition, it is recommended that the taxonomic notes included in the species descriptions are taken into account as these provide extra guidance on divisions of difficult taxa and discussion of the reasons and justification for these. SEM is not necessary for any of the identifications and we have not used features which are only visible using this technology as it is impractical in routine counting. Key differentiating features are given in bold type where several features are referred to at a particular division.

1. Test of secretion, without visible plates or particles   2

   Test with plates or particles   3
   NB: particles can sometimes be almost completely absent in some fossil
   specimens. However, unless the test is formed purely of smooth secretion
   the second option (3) should be followed here.

2. Test is disc-shaped, colour ranges from pale yellow to dark brown;
   aperture central   4

   Test a different shape; aperture not central   10

3. Test with plates or plate-like ornamentation   17

   Test with particles   25

4. Aperture **always ringed with obvious pores**. Test brown and is **often not quite
   circular**.   *Arcella catinus* type

   Disc usually circular; aperture without pores or with only faint pores visible   5

5. Disc circular, **flattened**; often delicate, transparent/pale brown in appearance.
   Aperture surrounded by shallow lip which may appear as a thickening in plan

view; usually without pores   *Arcella discoides* type

Test is **bowl-shaped or deeper**   6

NB: *Arcella* species are hard to rotate under a coverslip but the bowl shaped or deeper tests can be separated by careful focusing up and down.

6. Convex surface puffy with irregular bulges and hollows   *Arcella gibbosa* type

   Convex surface an evenly-curved dome   7

7. Hemisphere or deeper (can usually be rotated under cover-slip)
                                                                             Arcella hemispherica

   Shallower than hemisphere   9

9. Test **yellow/brown**. Test diameter >100µm
   Pores sometimes visible across test surface, but no apertural pores
                                                                                Arcella vulgaris

   Test brown, **diameter >180µm**; aperture with **approximately 30 pores**
                                                                                Arcella artocrea

10. Test with 2 apertures   11

    Test with 1 aperture   12

11. Test oblong, **amber-brown, without particles**   *Amphitrema flavum*

    Test often obscured by **mineral particles**. Apertures have **short collars**
                                                                       Amphitrema wrightianum

    Test with **mineral particles**. Apertures **without collars**   *Amphitrema stenostoma*

12. Aperture subterminal   13

    Aperture terminal   14

13. Test length 35-55µm. Plates usually visible   *Trinema/Corythion* type

    Test length 16-35µm. Plates hard to discern   *Trinema lineare*

14. Test colourless, circular or ovoid; smooth surface. Circular aperture sometimes surrounded by small collar. Length 14-23μm, breadth 12-18μm
Cryptodifflugia oviformis

Test strongly flattened; mouth at right-angles to long axis. Pinkish, yellowish or clear, length usually >25μm.
15

15. Test flask-shaped; narrow necked with **surface undulations**, particularly at posterior.
Hyalosphenia elegans

Test smooth; narrowing gradually towards aperture
16

16. **Walls are straight-sided. Pores always present at widest part of test**
Hyalosphenia papilio

Test more spherical than *H. papilio* and **walls curve smoothly towards aperture**
Hyalosphenia ovalis

Walls curve inward towards aperture
Hyalosphenia subflava

17. Test a mosaic of plates of variable shape
43

Test a patterned arrangement of regular plates
18

18. Plates four-sided
Quadrulella symmetrica

Test with aperture sub-terminal/oblique
13

Test with oval plates at aperture
19

Test with toothed plates at aperture
21

Test with short collar at aperture
Sphenoderia lenta

19. Test with spines
Placocista spinosa type

Test without spines
20

20 Test russet-brown; **length 35-60µm, breadth 32-48µm**   *Assulina muscorum*

Test russet-brown or pale brown, or occasionally clear; **length 65-105µm,**   •
breadth 58-74µm. Circular to broad oval in lateral view   *Assulina seminulum*

21. Test with **few stout spines**, each a **modified plate**, pointing backwards at posterior end

Euglypha acanthophora type*

Test with scattered thin articulated spines or without spines   22

22. Test **without spines. Length >45µm.** Not usually compressed when seen in non-lateral view

Euglypha tuberculata type

Test without spines. Length <45µm   *Euglypha rotunda* type

Test with spines   23

23. **Aperture plates thickened (focus on cross section and compare aperture plates with adjacent plates further up the test). Slender spines** scattered across surface. Test length 45-100µm   *Euglypha strigosa*

Spines robust or if more slender then not scattered across test surface. Aperture plates not thickened   24

24. **Spines always at test margin, test strongly compressed**

Euglypha compressa

Spines less robust, usually marginal but sometimes scattered in pairs over broad face of test; marginal angles less sharp   *Euglypha ciliata*

25. Test asymmetrical, composed of siliceous rods   *Lesquereusia spiralis*

Not like this   26

26. Test elongate to spherical with **small aperture at each end**   11

One aperture only   27

27. Test neat with **particles concentrated toward posterior end**   28

Particles similar throughout test   30

28. Test **wine-red/rose-red**, with orange apertural margin. Aperture at blunt
    angle to test   *Heleopera rosea*

    Test violet, greyish, yellow or colourless   29

29. Short (**length 50-75μm**) and narrow (25-30μm)   *Heleopera sylvatica*

    Test colourless, untidy with numerous mineral particles. **Aperture margins
    thickened, strongly convex, meeting side walls in a rounded, but definite angle**.
    Length 56-135μm   *Heleopera petricola*

    Test golden yellow or brown colour, **ovoid (sometimes almost circular)** and
    compressed. **Aperture margins not thickened**   *Heleopera sphagni*

30. Test spherical/elongate with terminal aperture at right angles to test length.   31

    Test approximately hemispheric. Aperture on flattest surface   39

    Test flattened with aperture on one side   40

    Test approximately spherical. **Aperture a curved slit**   *Bullinularia indica*

31. Pointed aboral region   32

    Rounded aboral region   33

32. Test predominantly composed of quartz particles   *Difflugia acuminata*

    Test predominantly composed of diatom frustules   *Difflugia bacilliararium*

33. Aperture edge **crenulate-toothed**, formed by **organic rim**   34

    Aperture edge not crenulate-toothed   35

34. Test **pyriform**, approximately twice as long as broad. Generally **<100μm**
                                                                      Difflugia rubescens

    Test **straight sided** or only slightly pyriform. **>100μm**   *Difflugia lanceolata*

35. Test **pyriform with walls flared towards aperture**, sometimes appearing as a collar. Small (16-30μm.) *Cryptodifflugia sacculus*

Test pyriform with distinct collar rather than flared walls
Pseudodifflugia fascicularis

Test pyriform, not as above 36

Test not pyriform 38

36. Test with horns *Difflugia leidyi*

Test predominantly of diatom frustules *Difflugia bacillifera*

Test with internal diaphragm separating neck from rest of test. May appear as only a faint v-shape in lateral view *Pontigulasia* spp*

Test not as above 37

37. Test small (<30μm and generally 22-25μm) with distinct neck. Flask shaped
Difflugia pulex

Test large (>30 and usually >60μm, often >150μm) *Difflugia oblonga* type

38. Spherical or only slightly longer than broad with clearly defined aperture
Cyclopyxis arcelloides type

More elongated (at least 1.5 times as long as broad). 65-100μm
Difflugia lucida type

More elongated (at least 1.5 times as long as broad). <65μm
Difflugia pristis type

More elongated. Test length <30μm
Pseudodifflugia fulva type

39. **Aperture 3-4 sided or a ragged circle**. Test brown with rough surface
Trigonopyxis arcula type

Aperture a smooth circle or oval *Cyclopyxis arcelloides* type

40. Test with spines 41

Test without spines 42

41. **Spines restricted to a single plane** as a crown around rim of test in lateral view
Centropyxis aculeata type

Spines scattered over test surface *Centropyxis hirsuta* type*

42. Test much longer than broad (approximately twice as long as broad or longer)
Centropyxis platystoma type

Test circular to ovoid (less than twice as long as broad) *Centropyxis cassis* type

43. Aperture subterminal/oblique 13

Aperture terminal. Plates irregular 44

44. Edge of aperture composed of particles **and recurved, forming a prominent lip**
Nebela griseola type

Edge of aperture **not recurved** 45

45. Aperture edged with plates 46

Aperture with smooth edges of secretion 47

46. Test colourless, **flask-shaped** with a distinct neck and **siliceous whiskers scattered over test surface.** Oval aperture with teeth which are difficult to see
*Nebela barbata**

Test narrowing gradually towards the aperture. **Without whiskers**
Nebela vitraea

47. Test flask-shaped, with a **distinct approximately parallel sided neck**. Test length
95-258µm, breadth 102-145µm *Nebela lageniformis**

Test colourless, **flask-shaped** with a distinct neck and **siliceous whiskers scattered over test surface.** Oval aperture with teeth which are difficult to see

Nebela barbata*

Test narrowing steadily towards the aperture   48

48. Aboral region of test edged with a flat keel or entire test margin strongly compressed   49

Aboral region of test without a keel or ridge   51

49. Pyriform **test margin strongly compressed**, clearly seen in broad lateral view by focusing up and down   *Nebela galeata**

Aboral region edged with a **sharp keel**   50

50. Keel **narrow**, extending **less than halfway** to the aperture   *Nebela marginata**

Keel **broad**, extending **more than halfway** to the aperture   *Nebela carinata*

51. A pair of large, conspicuous pores on the broad face of the test   *Nebela bigibbosa**

Without pores on the broad face of the test   52

52. Test as **broad as long, or broader**; narrowing abruptly to aperture   *Nebela flabellulum*

Breadth of test less than length   53

53. Test less than twice as long as broad; aperture length less than one-third maximum width of test   54

Test more than twice as long as broad; aperture more than one-third maximum width of test   55

54. With a **pair of lateral pores**, faintly visible as breaks in the side walls, near the mouth   *Nebela tincta*

Without lateral pores   *Nebela parvula*

55. Without lateral pores   56

With a pair of lateral pores, faintly visible as breaks in the side walls, near the aperture   57

NB: This is not always a reliable character as pores are difficult to see, for example in *N.militaris*, below. In addition pores are sometimes reported from *N.minor*. Hence small specimens of *N.minor* and large specimens of *N.militaris* may be confused, although this has rarely proved to be a problem in practice.

56. Test pyriform, tapering gently to wide, curved aperture. Distinguished from *N. collaris* by smaller size (**70-100µm** long) and broader aperture. Lateral pores sometimes visible   *Nebela minor*

Test ovoid or pyriform. Distinguished from *N. minor* by larger size (**93-184µm long**) and **strongly convex aperture**   *Nebela collaris*

57. Small (**length <72µm**, breadth 15-28µm). **Convex aperture** with thickened margins   *Nebela militaris*

Test colourless or yellow-brown, pyriform to flask-shaped. Large (>190µm)
                                                                Nebela tubulosa type

CHAPTER 5
DESCRIPTIONS OF TAXA AND IDENTIFICATION
NOTES

This following descriptions are intended to provide additional notes on identification to confirm identifications made in the key. Microphotographs are provided for all taxa commonly encountered in our studies with some SEM photographs to help illustrate particular features of some taxa. However, routine counting of testate amoebae will always be undertaken with a light microscope and it is not intended that the use of SEM is required for the taxonomy described here. We do not regard detailed descriptions based on fine scale structural characteristics (e.g. Ogden, 1983) as useful in this respect and none of the characters used for determining taxa require SEM. In addition, the discussion includes consideration of the rationale for the groupings we have adopted. The taxa are arranged by family and within family in alphabetical order. Key references are given for individual genera, species or species groups within the relevant descriptions. Other sources from which the notes are drawn are also acknowledged but it is recommended that other general identification sources are consulted, including de Graaf (1956), Grospietsch (1958), Corbet (1973), Ogden and Hedley (1980) and Ellison and Ogden (1987).

The morphospecies described here often include species which have been separated by other authors. This is not necessarily because we think that the original authorities for the additional species were wrong to erect a new species. In some cases we regard the names as synonymous. In others we believe there is a good case for separation but we have found that this is difficult to do consistently for routine counting of fossil samples, due to the problems described in Chapter 1. We list the former as 'synonyms' and the latter as 'other species included'. However, we recognise that there may be some species missing from these lists, although we have made every effort to include those reported from oligotrophic peats in the more easily accessible literature. We have not comprehensively referred to varieties or forms which have been given names in the past unless these lower order divisions have been extensively used in the discussion of sub-fossil testate amoebae for peatlands. Where a designation includes other species we have designated the taxon as a 'type'. All the original authorities are given in two forms. Normally the first time the species was described is given as the authority, even if the species was subsequently transferred to a different genus, and these are used in the species descriptions but placed within parentheses. However, if a species was subsequently renamed, the secondary authority is also given. While this does not strictly follow convention, we feel it is useful to be able to track nomenclatural changes through the literature as far as possible, since some confusion has arisen over the naming of many species and this affects the taxonomy described here as it applies to fossil tests (see for example discussion of *Difflugia globulus* Ehrenberg 1848 under *Cyclopyxis arcelloides* type). The dimensions given refer to the longest axis or to length x breadth where two measurements are given. All figures are reproduced at a comparable scale of x400 except where indicated.

AMPHITREMIDAE. One genus - *Amphitrema*

These are the only taxa with two pseudostomes, symmetrically positioned at ether end of a round to elongate test. The test is composed of proteinaceous material, sometimes with agglutinated particles. The smooth, brown test of *A. flavum* (Figure 7a) makes it easy to identify and it is one of the most common species occurring in ombrotrophic peatlands in northwest Europe. *A. wrightianum* and *A. stenostoma* can be more difficult to separate as they are both often thickly covered with particles (Figure 6b shows an example of this). Although they are separated by the presence or absence of a collar, this can be difficult to see where the xenosomes obscure the pseudostomes, even in optical section. This is mainly only a problem in surface samples and most fossil specimens of *A. wrightianum* have only a sparse covering of particles. There is some difference in shape with *A. wrightianum* generally more ovoid and *A. stenostoma* more elongate. However, this is not easy to provide a definition for and may not be a completely reliable character. Heal

(1961) grouped these two species when studying modern specimens and Ogden (1984) suggests they may be synonymous, but separation is generally possible using the criteria described here.

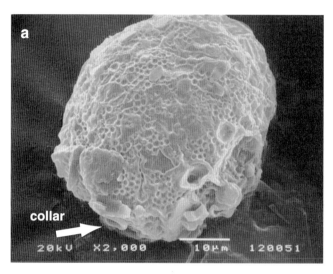

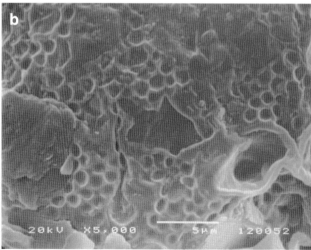

Figure 6: SEM photographs of: a) *Amphitrema wrightianum* with the short collar just visible on the lower left hand side of the test. b) *A. wrightianum* showing detail of test construction with xenosomes and cement with small pores.

Amphitrema flavum (**Archer 1877**) **Penard 1902** (Figure 7a)

This species is not easily confused with any other. However, Van Oye (1956) has reported a related species from New Zealand named *A. jollyi* but differing only in being of a slightly larger size. However, due it being morphologically identical and the description being based on a few individuals from a single sample, we would include this within *A. flavum*.

Synonymy:

Ditrema flavum Archer 1877

Amphitrema jollyi Van Oye 1956

Dimensions: 45-70μm (this study), 50-75μm (Grospietsch, 1958), 45-77μm (Corbet, 1973), 40-66x23-35μm (Ogden, 1984).

Test outline: elongate in broad lateral view with almost parallel sides.

Colour: amber-brown.

Test material: smooth, proteinaceous, without agglutinated particles.

Aperture: one circular to oval at both poles.

Amphitrema stenostoma **Nüsslin 1884** (Figure 7b)

Dimensions: 45-90μm (this study), 45-65μm (Grospietsch, 1958), 45-97μm (Corbet, 1973).

Test outline: elongate in broad lateral view.

Colour: colourless.

Test material: proteinaceous, coated with mineral particles.

Aperture: one at both poles, sometimes obscured by mineral particles. No collar.

Amphitrema wrightianum **Archer 1869** (Figure 7c, see also Figures 6a, 6b)

Dimensions: 50-90μm (this study), 60-70μm (Grospietsch, 1958), 50-95μm (Corbet, 1973), 43-70x35-53μm (Ogden, 1984).

Test outline: almost spherical to elongate with parallel sides in broad lateral view.

Colour: colourless or yellow to amber brown, especially in fossil specimens.

Test material: proteinaceous test often obscured by a mixture of siliceous particles, including diatoms, flagellate cysts, and quartz particles.

Aperture: one at both poles with short, but distinct, collars. Collar length approximately 5μm, width 10μm.

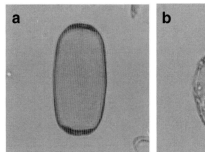
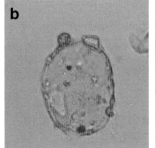
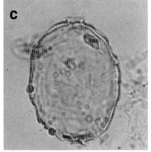

Figure 7: a) *Amphitrema flavum.* b) *Amphitrema stenostoma.* c) *Amphitrema wrightianum.*

ARCELLIDAE. One genus - *Arcella*

Another easily recognised family, with a circular test composed of proteinaceous material and lacking xenosomes. The central circular aperture is sometimes surrounded by pores. The generally smooth test is colourless, yellow or brown and may have bulges and angular folds (Deflandre, 1928). However, most of the taxa encountered in peatlands are smooth disc to bowl shaped tests. One of the problems with identification of individuals within this genus is that separation of many named species is based on slight variations in shell morphology, particularly the deepness of the bowl shape. Besides the problems of separation of such a phylogenetic series (see Chapter 1), in microscope slide preparations it is often not possible to rotate specimens into lateral view to observe this properly. Figure 8a to 8d shows *Arcella catinus* type from several angles, including a lateral view, and illustrate the variety of features which could be used to differentiate taxa if these views were readily visible. The taxonomy described here groups together a number of previously described species and has been applied to a large number of modern and fossil specimens during routine counting of tests. Some the synonyms noted below include varieties and forms which would key out under different names here. For example, *Arcella vulgaris forma undulata* Deflandre 1928 would be identified as *A.gibbosa* type in our key. We have not included all of these separate forms and varieties here. For more details on these see Deflandre (1928) and Decloitre (1976). Measurements all refer to maximum diameters of tests in polar view.

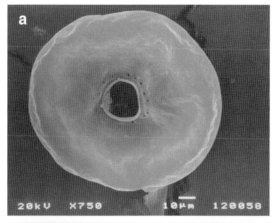

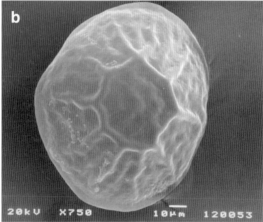

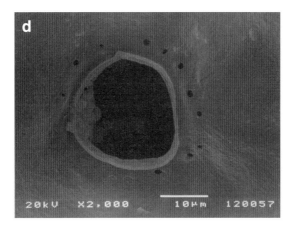

Figure 8: SEM photographs of *Arcella catinus* type: a) polar apertural view, b) polar aboral view, c) broad lateral view d) detail of pseudostome showing pores and short collar, the latter not visible under a light microscope.

Arcella catinus Penard 1890 type (Figure 9a, see also Figure 8)

This taxon is predominantly thought to relate to *A.catinus* Penard 1890, but in our view may also include a number of other species which are inseparable during routine counting. The dimensions given below refer to *A.catinus* but the other species mentioned overlap with these ranges. The key features are the clear ring of pores around the mouth and a circular to irregular test outline. Numbers of pores vary considerably between authors and we have not used this as a distinguishing character. Some of the species we have regarded as synonyms may have a more variable aboral region but again we have not found it possible to consistently separate species using such features during routine counting. For example Ogden and Hedley (1980), using SEM, describe a conical aboral region for *A.arenaria* Greef 1866 which is divided into segments but the large size of the test makes reliable manipulation of specimens impossible under a coverslip. The more complex structural detail is also clear in Figure 8.

Other species included:

Arcella arenaria Greef 1866

Dimensions: 73-114µm (this study), 110-123µm (de Graaf, 1956), 77-116µm (Grospietsch, 1958; Corbet, 1973), 73-114µm (Ogden and Hedley, 1980).

Test outline: Usually circular in broad lateral view, although many individuals have crumpled edges.

Colour: dark brown.

Test material: proteinaceous material produces a smooth surface.

Aperture: circular; 22-33μm diameter (this study), 23-27μm (de Graaf, 1956), 23-37μm (Ogden and Hedley, 1980). The pores are always clearly visible but variable in number (8-50, de Graaf, 1956; Ogden and Hedley, 1980).

Other features: Ogden and Hedley (1980) describe a shallow aboral region; this may appear folded when flattened under a coverslip (Corbet, 1973) but this is by no means always apparent.

Arcella discoides **Ehrenberg 1872 type** (Figure 9d)

This is one of the most common taxa within *Arcella* in peatlands and is quite variable in size. The key features are its circular outline and flattened disc-shape. Given the problems of rotating the larger *Arcella* species under a coverslip, we have grouped together all specimens which do not have an obvious bowl shaped test and lack obvious pores around the mouth into a single type designated *A. discoides* type. One taxon sometimes separated in previous peatland studies (Tolonen, 1986; Warner 1987) is *A.rotundata var. aplanata* Deflandre 1928 on the basis of a thickening of the rim of the mouth. While this is sometimes apparent depending on the angle of rest, we do not regard it as a consistent character.

Other species included:

Arcella rotundata Playfair 1917

Arcella rotundata var. aplanata Deflandre 1928

Arcella polypora Penard 1890

Arcella megastoma Penard in Wailes 1913

Dimensions: 78-105μm (this study), 38-73μm (de Graaf, 1956), 53-168μm (Corbet, 1973), 83-104μm (Ogden and Hedley, 1980), 105-110μm (Ellison and Ogden, 1987).

Test outline: circular in broad lateral view.

Colour: transparent, yellow or brown.

Test material: proteinaceous material produces a smooth surface.

Aperture: circular; sometimes bordered by a shallow lip (Ogden and Hedley, 1980). Diameter 21-31μm.

Other features: small pores on the test surface are described by Ogden and Hedley

(1980) but these may not be visible under light microscopy.

Arcella gibbosa **Penard 1890 type** (Figure 10)

Other species included:

Arcella bathystoma Deflandre 1928

Arcella crenata Playfair 1917

Dimensions: 87-90µm (this study), 92-100µm (de Graaf, 1956), 70-125µm (Grospietsch, 1958; Corbet, 1973), 90µm (Ogden and Hedley, 1980).

Test outline: circular in broad lateral view.

Colour: yellow or brown.

Test material: proteinaceous.

Aperture: circular, with a distinct rim. Diameter 20µm (this study); 25µm (de Graaf, 1956); 19µm (Ogden and Hedley, 1980). Pores absent.

Other features: Test is characterised by distinctive undulations on the aboral surface.

Arcella hemispherica **Perty 1852** (Figure 9e)

Dimensions: 55-65µm (this study), 46-78µm (de Graaf, 1956), 45-56µm (Grospietsch, 1958; Corbet, 1973), 50µm (Ellison and Ogden, 1987), 55-63µm (Ogden and Hedley, 1980).

Test outline: hemispherical in broad lateral view, circular in plan view but edges may be dented.

Colour: yellow or brown.

Test material: proteinaceous.

Aperture: circular and bordered by a small lip. No pores. Diameter 11-13µm (this study); 11-14µm (Ogden and Hedley, 1980).

Other features: test is covered by small pores which may be difficult to observe under light microscopy. Grospietsch (1958), Corbet (1973), Ogden and Hedley (1980) and Ellison and Ogden (1987) describe the test as hemispherical in lateral view and due to this and its smaller size, most individuals can be rotated under a coverslip.

Arcella vulgaris **Ehrenberg 1830, 1832a** (Figure 9b)

The two remaining *Arcella* types recognised here are those with bowl shaped but less than hemispheric tests. We are aware that this may seem an imprecise character and indeed there may be confusion between these species and *A. discoides* and *A. catinus*. However, the degree of curvature of the posterior is such that it is detectable even in plan view by careful focusing and examination of optical sections. The main difference between *A. vulgaris* and *A. artocrea* is the larger size and presence of pores in the latter species.

Dimensions: 150-183μm diameter (this study), 100-145μm (Grospietsch, 1958; Corbet, 1973), 104-136μm (Ogden and Hedley, 1980), 97-111μm, depth, 17-24μm (Ogden, 1984).

Test outline: circular - not perfectly circular in plan view. Bowl shaped with domed posterior region in lateral view (Ogden, 1984).

Colour: yellow, amber-brown or brown.

Test material: proteinaceous, with numerous pores over the test surface giving a honeycomb appearance.

Aperture: not perfectly circular; may be invaginated. No pores. Diameter *c.*35μm (this study), 22-32μm (Ogden and Hedley, 1980), 43-66μm (Ogden, 1984).

Arcella artocrea **Leidy 1876a** (Figure 9c)

Dimensions: 185-190μm diameter (this study), 180-200μm (Grospietsch, 1958), 184-216μm (Ogden and Hedley, 1980).

Test outline: circular in broad lateral view.

Colour: brown.

Test material: proteinaceous material produces a smooth surface; studded by pores across test surface.

Aperture: 33μm (this study), 36μm diameter (Ogden and Hedley, 1980), surrounded by 30 pores of assorted sizes.

Other features: Ogden and Hedley (1980) noted a conical aboral region which is dented, but the species is too large to rotate into aboral view under a coverslip. See *A.vulgaris* for further comments.

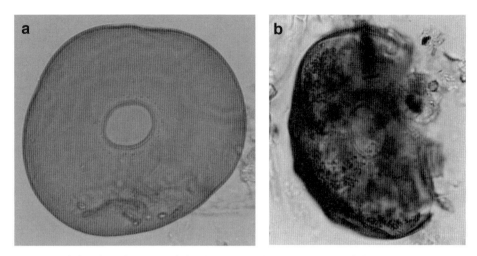

Figure 9: a) *Arcella catinus* type. b) *Arcella vulgaris.* c) *Arcella artocrea.* d) *Arcella discoides* type. e) *Arcella hemispherica.*

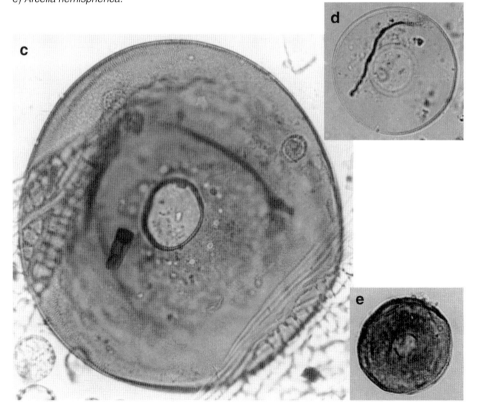

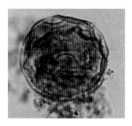

Figure 10: *Arcella gibbosa* type.

CENTROPYXIDAE. One genus - *Centropyxis*.

The division between the Centropyxidae and the Trigonopyxidae principally concerns the symmetry of the test. The Trigonopyxidae, in common with the Difflugiidae, have a symmetrical test, with an aperture at right angles to the length of the test. The Centropyxidae however, have an asymmetrical test in which one side is flattened and the aperture is on this flattened side, almost parallel with the length of the test. The colourless to yellow-brown test of the Centropyxidae is thus a flattened sphere or more commonly ovoid. The compressed apertural end is obvious in narrow lateral view but tests are more commonly observed in broad lateral view where the displacement of the aperture towards one end is also evident. The test is composed of proteinaceous material with agglutinated mineral particles. Spines are sometimes present but may not be as good a diagnostic feature as is sometimes suggested. We have divided them into four types and attempted a synonymy below but this is a complex group and there is an argument for even greater grouping, ignoring features such as spines altogether (Medioli and Scott, 1983). Despite this we have found that the taxonomy described here is workable and repeatable and prefer to keep this level of division.

Centropyxis aculeata **(Ehrenberg 1830,1832a) von Stein 1859 type** (Figure 11a,11b)

Forms of *Centropyxis* with spines can be divided into two groups based on whether spines occur all over the surface of the test or only in a single plane. This character has been used in the key to separate *C. aculeata* from *C. hirsuta* Deflandre 1929 but we have not encountered the latter in our work so far and it is not illustrated. Numbers of spines in *C. aculeata* type seem to be inconsistent and we have not used these as a character. Using this as the sole criteria, *C. hirsuta* would also include *Centropyxis gibba* Deflandre 1929, and *Centropyxis spinosa* (Cash and Hopkinson, 1905) Deflandre 1929, although these were separated along with other related species by Deflandre (1929). Until fossil examples of this have been encountered frequently in peats, it is not possible to provide a full assessment of the synonymy.

Synonymy:

Arcella aculeata Ehrenberg 1830, 1832a

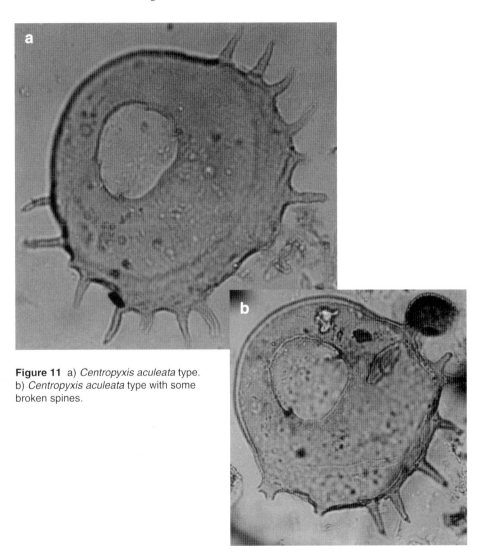

Figure 11 a) *Centropyxis aculeata* type. b) *Centropyxis aculeata* type with some broken spines.

Centropyxis discoides Penard 1890 and Deflandre 1929

Dimensions: 116-148x48-60μm (this study), 120-150x48-60μm (Grospietsch, 1958; Corbet, 1973), 92-178x77-137μm (Ogden and Hedley, 1980).

Test outline: ovoid or circular in broad lateral view. In narrow lateral view, test tapers towards aperture.

Colour: amber-brown (this study), translucent grey-green to dark brown (Corbet, 1973), yellow or brown (Ogden and Hedley, 1980).

Test material: proteinaceous and sometimes covered with quartz particles to produce a rough surface.

Aperture: sub-terminal, oval and 32-64μm in diameter; 35-70μm diameter (Ogden and Hedley, 1980).

Other features: *C. aculeata* has a variable number of spines always in a single plane.

Centropyxis cassis **(Wallich 1864) Deflandre 1929 type** (Figure 12a)

Spineless examples of *Centropyxis* fall within either *C. cassis* type or *C. platystoma* type which we have divided on the basis of length:breadth ratio. While this is a convenient and reasonably precise division, it may not in fact be very meaningful except as an arbitrary division of a continuum of change. However, on the basis that any such repeatable division may be ecologically useful we suggest that where possible the division is made, although it does require a broad lateral view. However, most specimens can be easily rotated to this position under a coverslip.

Synonymy:

Difflugia cassis Wallich 1864

Other species included:

C. aerophila Deflandre 1929

C. orbicularis Deflandre 1929

C. aerophila var. *sphagnicola* Deflandre 1929

C. aerophila var. *sylvatica* Deflandre 1929

Dimensions: 62-82x48-67μm (this study), 58-67x48-53μm (de Graaf, 1956), 60-86x50-73μm (Grospietsch, 1958), 60-85μm (Corbet, 1973), 79-117x57-90μm (Ogden and Hedley, 1980), 50-125μm (Ellison and Ogden, 1987).

Test outline: In broad lateral view, sides are parallel to convex and become semi-circular at both poles. In narrow lateral view, test tapers towards apertural region.

Colour: colourless-brown.

Test material: proteinaceous, covered by quartz grains to produce a rough surface.

Aperture: sub-terminal; semi-circular and surrounded by untidy particles.

Other features: Separated from *C. platystoma* type by length:breadth ratio <2:1. No spines.

Centropyxis platystoma **(Penard 1890) Deflandre 1929 type** (Figures 12b, 12c)

Synonymy:

Difflugia platystoma Penard 1890

Centropyxis constricta (Ehrenberg 1843, Leidy 1879a) Deflandre 1929

Dimensions: 57-74x29-56μm (this study), 63-95x36-64μm (Grospietsch, 1958), 60-86μm (Corbet, 1973), 62-81x34-48μm (Ogden and Hedley, 1980), <100μm (Ellison and Ogden, 1987).

Test outline: test pyriform, elongate or ovoid in broad lateral view and tapers markedly in narrow lateral view.

Colour: colourless to brown.

Test material: proteinaceous and coated by quartz particles.

Aperture: sub-terminal and circular; 19-27μm diameter (Ogden and Hedley, 1980). Apertural region often smoother than remainder of test.

Other features: Included as part of the *C. cassis* group by Corbet (1973) but split here on the basis of a length:breadth ratio >2:1. Ogden and Hedley (1980) note three main

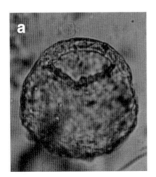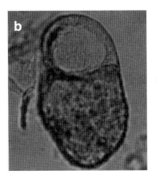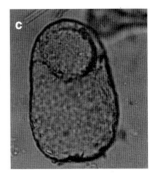

Figure 12: a) *Centropyxis cassis* type. b) *Centropyxis platystoma* type showing a relatively narrow test form. c) *Centropyxis platystoma* type showing a broader test form, but not exceeding the 1:2 breadth to length criterion used to separate *C.cassis* type.

areas of variation in the species: the degree of invagination of the aperture, the constriction of the neck and the shape of the test, but it seems likely that almost the entire genus may be a closely related phylogenetic series.

TRIGONOPYXIDAE - Two genera: *Trigonopyxis* and *Cyclopyxis*

The division between the Trigonopyxidae and the Centropyxidae is discussed above. However, we have included within the taxa described here, several species which are often placed in another family, the Phryganellidae and also some from the Difflugidae. In previous palaeoecological work (Warner, 1987; Tolonen, 1986) *Phryganella* has been separated on the basis of test composition including organic detritus, but we have found this criterion difficult to apply in practice and do not believe it is a useful character. Descriptions of test composition seem to vary considerably between authors and it seems unlikely that this can be used as a consistent distinguishing feature. This is discussed further under *Cyclopyxis arcelloides* type below. There is also some confusion in the literature regarding this taxon, since *Cyclopyxis arcelloides* and *Centropyxis arcelloides* are used interchangeably to describe the same species. For example, Corbet (1973) refers to *Centropyxis (Cyclopyxis) arcelloides* and this is apparently due to *Cyclopyxis* being regarded as a subgenus of *Centropyxis* (Corbet 1973). Deflandre (1929) originally suggested this distinction but virtually all later work has accepted *Cyclopyxis* as an independent genus in its own right (Decloitre, 1977b). This also follows the taxonomic conventions of the Committee of Systematics and Evolution of the Society of Protozoology (1980) and recognises *Centropyxis* as a genus of Centropyxidae and *Cyclopyxis* as a genus of Trigonopyxidae. However, we also include synonyms from *Centropyxis* on the basis that they have symmetrical tests. We only include two taxa within this potentially broad group which are separated on the basis of the shape of the aperture. Most of what we regard as synonyms for *Cyclopyxis arcelloides* are inseparable on the basis of size or morphology since the range of variation within these taxa overlaps considerably. Tests of both taxa described here are circular or hemispherical, composed of agglutinated particles with a central aperture (Ogden and Hedley, 1980).

Cyclopyxis arcelloides (Penard 1902) Deflandre 1929 type (Figure 13a, 13b)

This is a highly variable taxa and a large size range is encountered (see Table 7). In counting a large number of fossil specimens we have not been able to separate these into separate distinctive taxa based on size classes or morphological differences. They are thus grouped as a single taxa. The structure of the tests of *Cyclopyxis arcelloides* and related taxa are strikingly similar to *Difflugia* species. However, *Difflugia, Cyclopyxis* and *Phryganella* are separable by different characters of the pseudopodia in living specimens. Since these are absent in fossil material and empty tests from surface samples, a number of *Difflugia* species are inseparable from *Cyclopyxis*. These almost spherical *Difflugia* species may be grouped under *Difflugia globulus* (Ehrenberg 1848) Cash and Hopkinson 1909. The latter reference describes the rather convoluted and confusing history of nomenclature of this group which inlcudes *Difflugia globularis* Wallich 1864 and *Difflugia globulosa* Dujardin 1837. The former appeared as a misquote of Dujardin (1837) and the latter is regarded as confusing since the figures of Dujardin (1837) bear no resemblance to later descriptions (Cash and Hopkinson, 1909), although both are still used in later monographs! (Gauthier-Lièvre and Thomas, 1958).

Synonymy:

Centropyxis eurystoma Deflandre 1929

Centropyxis minuta Deflandre 1929

Centropyxis arcelloides Penard 1902

Centropyxis laevigata Penard 1890

Centropyxis aplanata Deflandre 1929

Centropyxis penardi Deflandre 1929

Centropyxis kahli Deflandre 1929

Other species included:

Phryganella hemisphaerica Penard 1902

Phryganella acropodia (Hertwig and Lesser 1874) Cash and Hopkinson 1909

Phryganella nidulus Penard 1902

Difflugia globulus (Ehrenberg 1848) Cash and Hopkinson 1909

Dimensions: see Table 7. Diameter varied between 35 and 107µm in our specimens.

Test outline: circular in broad lateral view; hemispherical in narrow lateral view.

Colour: colourless to yellow brown.

Test material: mineral particles, organic detritus and fungal hyphae.

Aperture: central, may be invaginated.

Other features: see notes under Trigonopyxidae for taxonomic problems.

Species	Diameter μm
Centropyxis eurystoma Deflandre 1929	40-80
Centropyxis arcelloides Penard 1902	65-100
Phryganella hemisphaerica Penard 1902	30-54
Centropyxis minuta Deflandre 1929	35-60
Centropyxis kahlii Wailes in Deflandre 1929	80-85
Phryganella acropodia (Hertwig and Lesser 1874) Cash and Hopkinson 1909	30-54

Table 7: Measurements for test diameter (μm) for synonyms within the *Cyclopyxis arcelloides* type. Data drawn from Cash and Hopkinson (1909), Deflandre (1929), Grospietsch (1958), Meisterfeld (1979), Ogden and Hedley (1980), Ogden (1984), Ellison and Ogden (1987).

Trigonopyxis arcula **(Leidy 1879a) Penard 1912 type** (Figure 13c, 13d)

This is distinguished by its normally non-circular mouth, which most often appears as a rough triangle but may also be four-sided or more irregular, sometimes forming a ragged circle (Bobrov *et al.*, 1995). We have never seen a smooth circular mouth so it is unlikely to be confused with *Cyclopyxis arcelloides* type, and the mouth is always much smaller in *Trigonopyxis* in any case. Hoogenraad and de Groot (1948) named a new species *T. microstoma* from New Zealand on the basis of a small, ragged, circular mouth but it is possible that this is a synonym of *T. arcula* or even conceivably of *Cyclopyxis arcelloides* as defined here. *T. minuta* Schönborn and Peschke, 1988 is separated by size as being <90μm (Schönborn and Peschke, 1988). Bobrov *et al.* (1999) separate *T. arcula* into three size classes (<90μm - *T. minuta*, 90-140μm - *T. arcula sensu lato,* >140μm var. *major* Chardez 1960) and find that larger tests inhabit wetter microhabitats. On this basis it may be worthwhile to split this taxon into these separate morphotypes.

Synonymy:

Difflugia arcula Leidy 1879a

Dimensions: 123-134μm (this study), 85-109μm (Hoogenraad and de Groot, 1940), 100-150μm (Grospietsch, 1958; Corbet, 1973), 95-168μm (Ogden and Hedley, 1980), 100-170μm (Ellison and Ogden, 1987), 85-120μm (Lüftnegger *et al.*, 1988), 54-185μm

(Bobrov *et al.*, 1995).

Test outline: circular in broad lateral view; hemispherical in narrow lateral view.

Colour: dark brown.

Test material: mineral particles bound by an organic cement.

Aperture: central; surrounded by a collar of organic cement; shape varies and may be triangular, square or an invaginated circle (Bobrov *et al.*, 1995). Diameter 21-42μm (Ogden and Hedley, 1980).

Figure 13: a) A small form of *Cyclopyxis arcelloides* type.
b) A larger form of *Cyclopyxis arcelloides* type.
c) *Trigonopyxis arcula* type showing individual with triangular aperture.
d) *Trigonopyxis arcula* type showing individual with sub-rounded aperture.

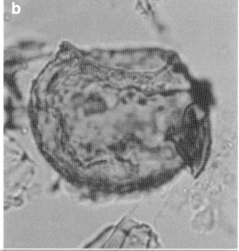

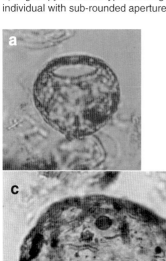

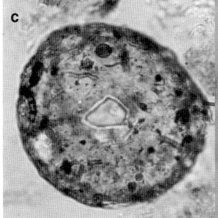

CRYPTODIFFLUGIIDAE. Three genera: *Cryptodifflugia, Difflugiella* **and** *Wailesella.* **Only** *Cryptodifflugia* **is recorded here.**

This is a group of small, *Difflugia*-like tests of variable form and only two taxa have been encountered in our studies on British peatlands. One of these, *Cryptodifflugia sacculus*, is clearly very close to *Difflugia* in terms of test construction and it is therefore is considered within that part of the key. However, both taxa are described here for consistency. *C. oviformis* type is very different to *C. sacculus* as it is lacks large xenosomes and is a smooth ovoid with a small collar around the circular mouth. This last feature is described by Ogden and Hedley (1980) but not by some other authors. Grospietsch (1964) provides a monograph on this group and Page (1966) provides a key, but since the separation of the genus from *Difflugia* and other related genera, this is not very useful for fossil specimens and empty tests.

Cryptodifflugia oviformis **Penard 1890** (Figure 14a)

The published size range of this species is up to 23μm in length and not more than 30μm (Page, 1966). However, we have found individuals up to 34μm in length.

Dimensions: length 15-34x12-25μm (this study), length 14.5-22.2x12.8-17.6μm (Ogden and Hedley, 1980), 15-18x8-15μm Grospietsch (1964), 15-23μm (Page, 1966).

Test outline: ovoid in broad lateral view.

Colour: colourless.

Test material: proteinaceous, with tiny mineral particles sometimes apparent.

Aperture: circular and terminal.

Cryptodifflugia sacculus **Penard 1902** (Figure 14b)

Dimensions: length 18-25x15-20μm (this study), 17-26 (Penard, 1902), 16-30x15-22μm (Grospietsch ,1964).

Test outline: elongate pyriform in lateral view, with short neck flared towards mouth.

Colour: clear to brown, grey.

Test material: proteinaceous, with agglutinated mineral particles.

Aperture: terminal; circular and surrounded by mineral particles, giving appearance of collar.

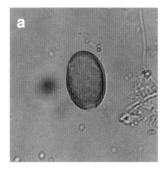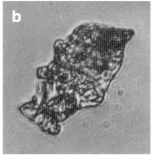

Figure 14: a) *Cryptodifflugia oviformis* (x1000). b) *Cryptodifflugia sacculus* (x1000).

DIFFLUGIIDAE and GROMIIDAE

These two families are difficult to separate in fossil and empty tests since the main division between them is on the basis of pseudopodial characteristics. The Difflugiidae are within the class Lobosea and have lobose pseudopodia while the Gromiidae (includes *Pseudodifflugia*) are within the Filosea and have filose pseudopodia. In terms of test characteristics they are inseparable in most cases and there is no logic in doing so for a scheme based on test features alone. In some cases, there could also be confusion with *Cyclopyxis arcelloides* and, as mentioned above, there is also overlap with the Cryptodifflugiidae. Medioli and Scott (1983) deal predominantly with *Difflugia* and related genera in their treatment of lake dwelling testate amoebae and have grouped together a large number of species separated by others working on similar material (Ellison and Ogden, 1987), arguing that there is a large degree of intra-specific variation and that phylogenetic series cannot be sensibly separated except at a gross scale. Although the range of morphological variation in peatland taxa is certainly less than that described by Medioli and Scott (1983), we agree that it is difficult to separate consistently or logically at the lowest levels equivalent to some of the more recent published descriptions (e.g. Ogden, 1983). However, since this group are a relatively small proportion of the overall assemblages we have probably not encountered anything like the full range of morphological variation. It is therefore likely that the treatment of this group may change in future, although for the moment the taxonomy described here has proved workable in our analyses.

The general characteristics of this group are a circular, ovoid or pyriform test, composed of agglutinated mineral particles, occasionally diatom frustules and rarely including organic fragments. The aperture is terminal and circular in the taxa described here but may be more variable (Medioli and Scott, 1983). There are four genera in the Difflugiidae (*Difflugia, Pontigulasia, Curcubitella, Sexangularia*) although only *Difflugia*-like individuals have been recorded by us. There is one genus (*Pseudodifflugia*) within the Gromiidae. Key references for the group are Penard (1902), Gauthier-Lièvre and Thomas (1958), and Ogden (1983), although many of the descriptions in the later literature may serve to confuse rather than clarify.

Difflugia acuminata Ehrenberg 1838 type (Figure 15a)

This is placed within *D. protaeiformis* Lamarck 1816 by Medioli and Scott (1983). All the individuals found by us conform to *D.acuminata*.

Synonymy: Many varieties and similar species have been described by Penard (1899, 1902), Gauthier-Lièvre and Thomas (1958) and Ogden (1983). It would be difficult and confusing to provide a full list.

Dimensions: 137x75 (this study), 100-300x72µm, (Cash *et al.,* 1909), 150-400µm (Grospietsch, 1958), 100-400µm (Corbet, 1973), 232x72µm, (Ogden and Hedley, 1980).

Test outline: test pyriform or cylindrical with a pointed aboral region.

Colour: transparent.

Test material: composed of quartz particles and fragments of diatoms.

Aperture: circular aperture.

D. bacillariarum Perty 1849a

Synonymy: As with *D. acuminata,* many similar species have been described and there is considerable confusion between *D. bacillariarum* and other species. We have given the name *D. bacillariarum* to all acuminate species with diatom frustules as the dominant xenosomes, although according to the literature, *D. bacillariarium* is often much smaller than *D. acuminata.*

Dimensions: 67-98x38-49µm (this study), 100-133x37-43µm (Hoogenraad and de Groot, 1940), 90-130µm (Grospietsch, 1958; Corbet, 1973), 67-69x40-44µm (Ogden and Hedley, 1980), 70-140µm (Ellison and Ogden, 1987), 73-103µm (Ogden, 1980).

Test outline: ovoid or circular in narrow lateral view; ovoid in broad lateral view.

Colour: transparent, colourless or amber.

Test material: organic cement, with thin siliceous plates overlaid by diatom frustules (Ogden, 1980; Ogden and Hedley, 1980; Ellison and Ogden, 1987).

Aperture: terminal; size and shape dependent on size and arrangement of diatom frustules which surround it (Ogden, 1980). Diameter 17-24μm (Ogden, 1980); 22-24μm (Ogden and Hedley, 1980).

Difflugia bacillifera **Penard 1890** (Figure 15b)

Synonymy: In contrast to other taxa described here, there are relatively few species which fit the description of *D.bacillifera* as described by Penard (1890). The definition we have used here of any pyriform, non-acuminate specimen coated in diatom frustules can be consistently applied to all our samples. Penard (1902) has noted that the species is particularly abundant in *Sphagnum* and it may be that this morphospecies (or perhaps ecophenotype) is relatively stable in this habitat.

Dimensions: 130-200x60-90μm (this study), 150-160x73-83μm (Hoogenraad and de Groot, 1940), 120-180μm (Grospietsch, 1958; Corbet, 1973), 118-168x60-79μm (Meisterfeld, 1979), 117-176x54-80μm (Ogden, 1980), 130-194x59-91μm (Ogden and Hedley, 1980), 125-200μm (Ellison and Ogden, 1987).

Test outline: pyriform in broad lateral view, with a distinct long, cylindrical neck.

Colour: colourless or brown.

Test material: siliceous: diatom frustules, which often conceal test outline.

Aperture: terminal; circular, surrounded by small quartz particles (Ogden and Hedley, 1980). Diameter 24-38μm (Meisterfeld, 1979), 17-27μm (Ogden, 1980), 25-36μm (Ogden and Hedley, 1980).

Difflugia lanceolata **Penard, 1890** (Figure 16a)

D.lanceolata and *D.rubescens* are distinguished by the organic rim around the mouth which forms a series of shallow teeth. *D. rubescens* is distinctly pyriform and always less than 100μm in length while *D. lanceolata* is straight sided and normally much larger. *D. rubescens* is common in surface and fossil samples but *D. lanceolata* is rare and only found in more nutrient rich sites.

Dimensions: 130μm (this study), 140-160μm, (Cash *et al.,* 1909), 116-159x46-72μm (Ogden and Hedley, 1980),108-155x56-92μm (Ogden, 1983).

Test outline: lanceolate, straight sided, tapering to a point, rounded aborally.

Colour: yellow or transparent.

Test material: composed of small pieces of quartz and flat diatom frustules.

Aperture: circular with a crenulate mouth.

Other features: characterized by uniform size and outline.

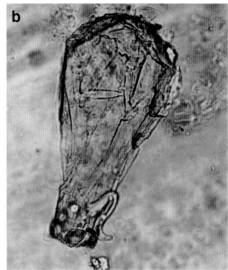

Figure 15:
a) *Difflugia acuminata.*
b) *Difflugia bacillifera.*

Difflugia leidyi **Wailes 1912a** (Figure 16b)

Pyriform tests with two horns are of consistent size and shape in our samples and conform to the descriptions of *D. leidyi* in Wailes (1912a).

Dimensions: 80-115x60-90μm (this study), 95x73μm (Hoogenraad and de Groot, 1940), 90-110μm (Grospietsch, 1958).

Test outline: ovoid or pyriform in broad lateral view with two horns at posterior.

Colour: colourless or brown.

Test material: siliceous mineral particles and diatom frustules.

Aperture: terminal; spherical with irregular margin produced by quartz particles. Diameter 35-40μm.

Difflugia lucida **Penard 1890 type** (Figure 16c)

The separation of the non-pyriform taxa lacking distinctive constructions or acuminate shapes within *Difflugia* is extremely confused in the literature. We agree to a certain extent with Medioli and Scott (1983) who argue for much greater grouping of species. Although we have previously attempted to sub-divide these specimens on the basis of slight variations in size and relative proportions of length:width:aperture, we have concluded that a division into three species only is worthwhile and even this may be somewhat spurious. *D. lucida* type is the largest (65-100μm), *D. pristis* type is smaller (generally 45-65μm although sometimes as small as 30μm) and much more abundant. *Pseudodifflugia fulva* is the smallest of the taxa used here. As with other morphospecies within *Difflugia* described here, we would expect these to include a number of other species separated by Gauthier-Lièvre and Thomas (1958) and Ogden (1983). It is also possible that we may combine these taxa at a later date should there prove to be little ecological purpose in this separation. The size criteria we have used to separate *D. lucida* type and *D. pristis* type are not entirely consistent with the earlier literature but seem to concur with later descriptions. For example, Penard (1890) gives 50-70μm, Cash and Hopkinson (1909) give 60-80μm and Gauthier-Lièvre and Thomas (1958) give three separate size ranges (44-50, 55-70, 83-90μm) for *D. lucida*. The names of our taxon types do not therefore strictly adhere to all published descriptions and do not equate precisely with these.

Dimensions: 80-100x50μm, 25μm diameter aperture (this study), 65-85μm (Grospietsch, 1958), 67-91x40-55x23-37μm (Ogden, 1983).

Test outline: ovoid, curved aborally, laterally compressed.

Colour: transparent.

Test material: composed of smooth flat quartz particles and occasional diatom frustules.

Aperture: diameter 17-25μm (Ogden, 1983).

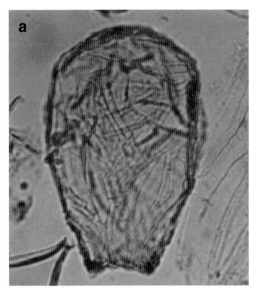

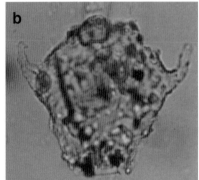

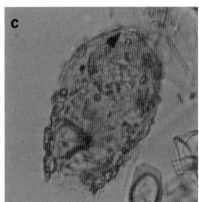

Figure 16: a) *Difflugia lanceolata.* b) *Difflugia leidyi.* c) *Difflugia lucida* type.

Difflugia oblonga **Ehrenberg 1830, 1832b type** (Figure 17a)

Ogden and Hedley (1980) note the considerable variation displayed by this species and this is discussed in some detail by Medioli and Scott (1983), who also produce a long list of synonyms, including *D. pyriformis* Perty 1849b. We mainly follow Medioli and Scott's definition with the exception of the separation of *D. bacillifera*, although we have not observed the same very large range of morphological variation. We have also found that a division with the smaller taxon *D. pulex* is easy to apply. In some work we have separated *D. penardi* Cash and Hopkinson 1909, length 60-85µm, as intermediate between *D. oblonga* and *D. pulex* but this is a much less clear division.

Synonymy: There are probably numerous other described species which would fall within this taxon. We initially separated some of these including *D. gassowskii* Ogden 1983 (renamed from *D. longicollis* Gassowsky 1936 (Ogden and Hedley, 1980)) based on size and slight morphological differences. However, having observed the large range of continuous variation which occurs, we have grouped all larger specimens under *D. oblonga* type.

Dimensions: 90-240x45-146µm (this study), 245-270x170µm (Hoogenraad and de Groot, 1940), 100-400µm (Grospietsch, 1958; Corbet, 1973), 190-237x92-146µm (Ogden and Hedley, 1980), 100-300µm (Ellison and Ogden, 1987).

Test outline: pyriform to a narrow ovoid.

Colour: brown.

Test material: angular quartz grains.

Aperture: terminal; circular, surrounded by small quartz grains; apertural rim smooth. Diameter 28-38µm (this study), 32-42µm (Ogden and Hedley, 1980).

Diffluia pristis **Penard 1902 type** (Figure 17b, 17c)

See *D.lucida* type for comments. A recent monograph on *Difflugia* (Ogden, 1983) includes descriptions of this species which are very different to the original descriptions in Penard (1890; 1902) as they describe a much smaller, pyriform species which could be *D. pulex.*

Other species included:

D. fallax Penard 1890

D. angulostoma Gauthier-Lièvre and Thomas 1958

Dimensions: 51-58x36-45µm (this study), 45-65µm (Penard, 1902), 60-65x30µm (Cash and Hopkinson, 1909).

Test outline: ovoid, curved aborally.

Colour: red, brown or opaque.

Test material: organic cement visible, organic matter, mineral particles.

Aperture: aperture often not distinct, but is circular, *c.*15µm.

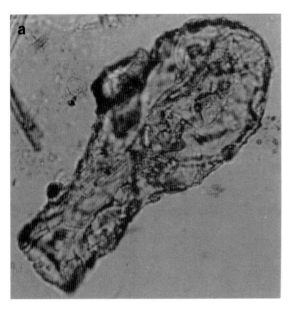
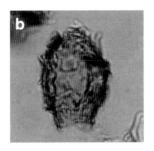
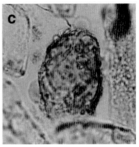

Figure 17: a) *Difflugia oblonga* type. b) *Difflugia pristis* type with sub-acuminate posterior. c) *Difflugia pristis* type with rounded posterior, showing an example of morphological variability within the taxon.

Difflugia pulex **Penard 1902** (Figure 18b)

This is a small pyriform species which is easy to overlook on crowded slides but is consistent in its size and shape and is therefore separated from the larger *D. oblonga* type. The shape of the test is always sharply pyriform as portrayed in Penard's typical examples (1902, Figs. 1 and 2, p230). Ogden (1983) illustrates examples named as *D. pulex* which differ from this, in which the shape of the test is obscured by diatom frustules and a heavy coating of siliceous xenosomes. They are also larger than Penard's original definition allows although they are included in the data below. We have not found similar examples in our samples.

Dimensions: <30μm (this study), 20-40μm (Ellison and Ogden, 1987), 28-43x21-30μm (Ogden 1983), 22-25μm and never >30μm Penard (1902).

Test outline: pyriform with a short collar in broad lateral view. Spherical in narrow lateral view.

Colour: colourless to brown.

Test material: small siliceous particles arranged to give an untidy test surface.

Aperture: terminal; diameter is much narrower than broadest part of test.

Difflugia rubescens Penard 1891 (Figure 18a)

See *D.lanceolata* for comments.

Dimensions: 70-90x38-54µm (this study), 80-93x43-60µm (Hoogenraad and de Groot, 1940), 71-78x42-46µm (de Graaf, 1956), 65-100µm (Grospietsch, 1958), 65-105µm (Corbet, 1973), 70-91x38-54µm (Ogden and Hedley, 1980), 60-105µm (Ellison and Ogden, 1987).

Test outline: pyriform in broad lateral view; circular in polar view.

Colour: yellow or light brown. Brick-red cytoplasmic granules sometimes visible through test in living individuals; not visible in fossil specimens.

Test material: thin coating of quartz particles and diatom frustules.

Aperture: terminal, circular and crenulated to produce tooth-like structures (Corbet, 1973), (Ogden and Hedley, 1980). Diameter 14-20µm (Ogden and Hedley, 1980).

Pseudodifflugia fascicularis Penard 1902 (Figure 18c)

This species is mainly distinguished by its prominent collar (Cash *et al.*, 1915) which should not be confused with the flared neck of *Cryptodifflugia sacculus*.

Dimensions: <35x *c*.25µm, (this study), 17-25µm (Penard, 1902), 23-40x2/3 of length, (Cash *et al.*, 1915).

Test outline: pyriform, short neck with conspicuous rim or collar of mineral particles.

Colour: Grey or colourless.

Test material: quartz grains with larger particles around mouth.

Aperture: terminal, circular, with collar, aperture *c*.12µm or half maximum breadth of test (Cash *et al.*, 1915).

Pseudodifflugia fulva (Archer 1870) Penard 1901 type (Figure 18d)

See *Difflugia lucida* for comments.

Dimensions: 28-30x24-27µm (this study), 15-30x12-20µm (Cash *et al.*, 1915), 15-23µm (Penard, 1901), 36x30µm (Ogden and Hedley, 1980)

Test outline: ovoid to circular in broad lateral view. Untidy outline.

Colour: brown to yellow-brown.

Test material: proteinaceous and sometimes thickly covered with agglutinated mineral particles.

Aperture: 6-12μm (Cash *et al.*, 1915), terminal and approximately circular (Ogden and Hedley, 1980).

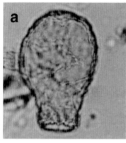
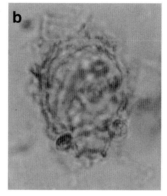
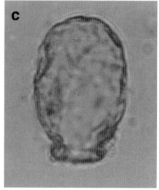
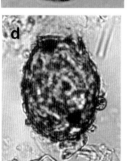

Figure 18:
a) *Difflugia rubescens* (x400).
b) *Difflugia pulex* (x1000).
c) *Pseudodifflugia fascicularis* (x1000).
d) *Pseudodifflugia fulva* type (x1000).

EUGLYPHIDAE. Five genera. *Euglypha, Assulina, Placocista, Sphenoderia* and *Tracheleuglypha*.

The main characteristic that differentiates this taxa family from others is the regular pattern of siliceous plates. Although several other taxa also possess this character (*Trinema, Corythion*), only in *Quadrulella* and the Euglyphidae are the plates so clearly seen. *Euglypha* species have toothed plates at the mouth and are easily separated from other taxa on this basis. *Sphenoderia* and *Tracheleuglypha* have a collar of organic cement. The test is usually oval to almost circular in broad lateral view and siliceous spines are sometimes present. Identification of the numerous species of *Euglypha* which have been described (*e.g.* Decloitre, 1962a) is not easy. We have used the presence or absence of spines to characterise some of the morphotypes, but this does not exactly follow some other authors who propose glabrous varieties of species which would normally have spines. In practice, we have found only relatively low numbers of spined or ciliate forms and most of these are *E. strigosa*. Decloitre (1962a) divides this genus into two groups. Group 1 has spines which are modified scales or, if spines are not present, a test with circular cross section. Group 2 has spines which are articulated at the base or an oval test if spines are absent. These groups are further subdivided on the basis of combinations of round or oval mouths and cross sections. Since identification depends on examination of the test in plan view from the apertural end, we have found these criteria very difficult to apply in practice. Even if the test can be rotated into a suitable position, the test may be distorted in fossil specimens and sometimes the assessment of roundness is rather difficult and therefore likely to be inconsistently applied between observers. The taxonomy we describe below thus groups together a number of species which may be separable if Decloitre's criteria are applied. One taxon mentioned in the key (*E. acanthophora* (Ehrenberg 1843) Perty 1849a) has not been found by us in oligotrophic peats and is therefore not described in detail below. On the basis of the criteria given it would include *E. aspera* Penard 1890, *E. brachiata* Leidy 1879a and several other species. See Decloitre (1962a) for further details if species with spines formed of modified scales are encountered.

Assulina muscorum Greeff 1888 (Figure 19a)

Dimensions: 46-58x34-44μm (this study), 35-60μm (Grospietsch, 1958), 28-58x19-50μm (Cash *et al.,* 1915), 45-53x32-48μm (Ogden and Hedley, 1980).

Test outline: ovoid in broad lateral view and flattened in narrow lateral view.

Colour: russet-brown or pale brown, occasionally clear.

Test material: siliceous oval plates, arranged in neat rows; organic cement at collar.

Aperture: terminal; oval, diameter 16-20μm (this study); 12-18μm (Ogden and Hedley, 1980).

Other features: Corbet (1973) and Ogden and Hedley (1980) note that, although test plates are normally neatly arranged, irregularities may appear. *Valkanovia elegans* Schönborn and Peschke 1990 can be distinguished from *A. muscorum* because it is 'colourless and has a thin, more or less smooth aperture rim' (Schönborn and Peschke 1990, p.100) but we have not used this distinction here. As with the *Trigonopyxis arcula* group, this further division may be meaningful in relation to hydrological parameters (Bobrov *et al.,* 1999).

Assulina seminulum **(Ehrenberg 1848) Leidy 1879a** (Figure 19b, 19c)

Synonymy:

Difflugia seminulum Ehrenberg 1848

Assulina seminulum var.*Scandinavica* Penard 1890

Dimensions: 60-68x58-71μm (this study), 65-105μm (Grospietsch, 1958), 60-90μm and sometimes up to 150μm (Cash *et al.*, 1915), 72-82x62-74μm (Ogden and Hedley, 1980).

Test outline: ovoid in broad lateral view; compressed in narrow lateral view.

Colour: reddish to yellowish-brown or colourless.

Test material: siliceous, oval plates; organic cement at collar.

Aperture: terminal, oval, surrounded by organic cement, diameter 21-23μm (Ogden and Hedley, 1980).

Other features: separated from *A. muscorum* by larger size, relative sphericity of test outline and normally pale/colourless test.

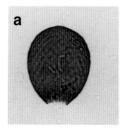 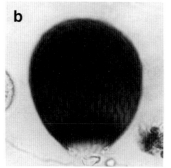 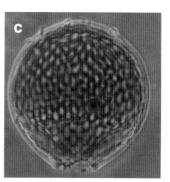

Figure 19: a) *Assulina muscorum* b) *Assulina seminulum.* c) *Assulina seminulum* (Phase contrast) showing plate structure.

Euglypha ciliata **(Ehrenberg 1848) Leidy 1878** (Figure 20b)

Synonymy:

Difflugia ciliata Ehrenberg 1848

Dimensions: 40-90μm (this study), 60-100μm (Grospietsch, 1958), 40-90μm (Corbet, 1973).

Test outline: ovoid in broad lateral view; compressed in narrow lateral view with short, slender spines often scattered in pairs over surface.

Colour: colourless.

Test material: regularly-arranged hexagonal siliceous plates.

Aperture: terminal; oval and compressed; bordered by plates to produce a toothed margin.

Euglypha compressa **Carter 1864** (Figure 20c)

Dimensions: length 70-132μm (this study; Corbet 1973), 70-130μm (Grospietsch, 1958), length 74-112x38-69μm (Ogden and Hedley, 1980), length 105μm (Ellison and Ogden, 1987).

Test outline: ovoid in broad lateral view; compressed in narrow lateral view; spines only present at margins of test.

Colour: colourless.

Test material: oval siliceous plates; siliceous spines.

Aperture: terminal; oval and surrounded by 11-12 apertural plates (Ogden and Hedley, 1980).

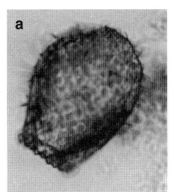 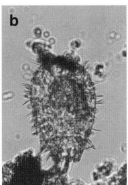 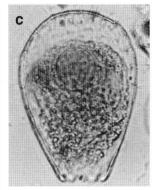

Figure 20: a) *Euglypha strigosa*. b) *Euglypha ciliata*. c) *Euglypha compressa*.

Euglypha rotunda **Wailes and Penard 1911 type** (Figure 21a, 21b)

The division between the spineless species of *Euglypha* has been based on the criteria of test and mouth cross sections (Decloitre, 1962a) and also size. We have avoided using the former criterion due to the practical problems of applying them consistently in routine counting. Hence we have grouped *E. laevis* Perty 1849b with *E. rotunda* Wailes and Penard 1911 which could be separated by oval and round mouths respectively. The division here between *E. rotunda* type and *E. tuberculata* type is based on size. Although there may be some overlap in ranges, in practice we have found this is a workable criterion and despite some possibility of misidentification of intermediate individuals, the separation has lead to the identification of distinct ecological niches for the two taxa (Woodland *et al.*, 1998).

Other species included:

Euglypha laevis (Ehrenberg 1845) Perty 1849b

Dimensions: 20-50µm (this study), 22-52µm (Grospietsch, 1958; Corbet 1973), 34-54x14-24µm (Ogden and Hedley, 1980), 35µm (Ellison and Ogden, 1987), 28-57µm (Lüftnegger *et al.*, 1988).

Test outline: ovoid in broad lateral view; circular to oval in narrow lateral view. No spines.

Colour: colourless.

Test material: approximately 120 oval, siliceous plates.

Aperture: terminal; circular and surrounded by 8-14 plates. Diameter 6-10µm (Ogden and Hedley, 1980).

Euglypha strigosa **(Ehrenberg 1872) Leidy 1878** (Figure 20a)

Synonymy:

Difflugia strigosa Ehrenberg 1872

Dimensions: 45-100µm (this study; Corbet, 1973), 50-85µm (Grospietsch, 1958), 73-89x32-52µm Ogden and Hedley (1980), 75µm (Ellison and Ogden, 1987), 72-80µm (Lüftnegger *et al.*, 1988).

Test outline: ovoid in broad lateral view; compressed in narrow lateral view; slender spines scattered over surface.

Colour: colourless.

Test material: approximately 300 oval siliceous plates (Ogden and Hedley, 1980).

Aperture: terminal; round and surrounded by 10-14 thickened plates, 14-17µm diameter.

Other features: test covered by slender spines, which project from plate junctions either singly or in pairs. Ogden and Hedley (1980) note that the spines are easily dislodged during preparation for SEM work.

Euglypha tuberculata **Dujardin 1841 type** (Figure 21c)

See comments under *E.rotunda. E.scutigera* Penard 1911 would key out to be within this taxon, but it is possible to separate it by its scutiform scales. However, this feature is often difficult to see clearly, especially in fossil specimens and we include it under this type.

Other species included:

E. scutigera Penard in Wailes and Penard 1911.

Dimensions: 45-100µm (this study; Grospietsch, 1958; Corbet, 1973), 74-95µm (Ogden and Hedley, 1980).

Test outline: ovoid in broad lateral view; circular in narrow lateral view.

Colour: colourless.

Test material: approximately 100 siliceous plates.

Aperture: terminal; circular; bordered by 8-12 finely-toothed plates. Diameter 18-21µm.

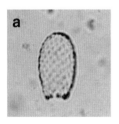 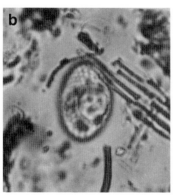 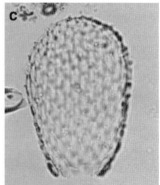

Figure 21: a) *Euglypha rotunda* type. b) *Euglypha rotunda* type from apertural end showing round mouth. This view is rarely visible, although could be used to separate *E.rotunda* from *E.laevis*, which has an oval mouth. c) *Euglypha tuberculata* type.

Placocista spinosa **(Carter 1865) Leidy 1879a type** (Figure 22a)

Placocista jurassica Penard 1905 is a related species with smaller spines over the whole of the surface of the test. We have not differentiated between these species here. In fossil specimens it is often found without spines.

Synonymy:

Euglypha spinosa Carter 1865

Other species included:

Placocista jurassica Penard 1905

Dimensions: 143-160x87-110µm (this study; Ogden and Hedley, 1980), 100-155µm (Grospietsch, 1958), 116-174µm (Corbet, 1973).

Test outline: ovoid in broad lateral view, with semi-circular aboral region and blunt, but concave apertural region. Pairs of spines present at test margins.

Colour: colourless or transparent.

Test material: oval, siliceous plates (Ogden and Hedley, 1980); overlapping and arranged in regular rows.

Aperture: terminal; wide, concave; 58-79µm diameter.

Sphenoderia lenta **Schlumberger 1845** (Figure 22b)

This is the only species of *Sphenoderia* found by us on British mires, but several related species occur and have been found on other ombrotrophic peatland sites elsewhere. *S.fissirostris* Penard 1890 has been found in some abundance on New Zealand peatlands (Charman, 1997) and is differentiated by having much fewer and more oval plates (3 or sometimes 4 rows) as well as being generally much smaller in size. Another related species, *Tracheleuglypha dentata* (previously *S.dentata* Penard 1890) has a collar of teeth formed of secretion instead of a smooth collar and has been shown to be an important component of saltmarsh faunas in Britain (Charman *et al.*, 1998). For descriptions of these species see Cash *et al.* (1915) or Grospietsch (1958).

Dimensions: 49-51x30-33µm (this study), 30-64µm (Corbet, 1973), 47-55x35-40µm (Ogden and Hedley, 1980), 35-55x 24-40µm (Ogden, 1984).

Test outline: circular, or ovoid, with a conspicuous collar in broad lateral view.

Colour: colourless.

Test material: approximately 60 circular or oval (Corbet, 1973) siliceous plates (Ogden and Hedley, 1980).

Aperture: terminal, linear (Ogden and Hedley, 1980); 16-19µm diameter.

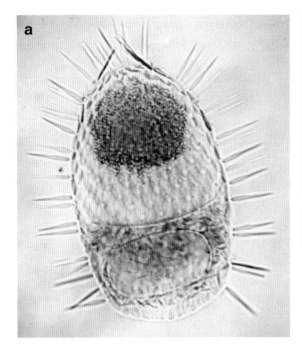

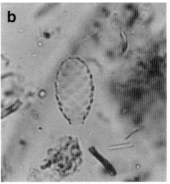

Figure 22:
a) *Placocista spinosa* type.
b) *Sphenoderia lenta*.

HYALOSPHENIIDAE. Five genera. *Heleopera, Hyalosphenia, Lesquereusia, Nebela, Quadrulella*)

This is also a large family which are highly variable in appearance despite being within the same family. There are few criteria which unite the family and further notes on genera are included below.

Heleopera

The main characteristic of this genus is the asymmetric arrangement of the xenosomes which are concentrated towards the aboral end of the test. This is almost always an obvious feature but may become less easy to see in some fossil specimens. The rest of the test often has plates but these are usually indistinct or impossible to see in fossil specimens. Separation of the species described here is based on the shape of the test and the nature of the mouth. In addition, we have also referred to colour differences between some species. While this may be unreliable for some other species groups, the colour differences in *Heleopera* are strong and consistent with few intermediate specimens. Warner (1987) suggested that the use of a stain in preparation means that separation of *H.rosea* is not possible, but since colouration is so strong in stained and unstained specimens when it does occur and is not present at all in other specimens from the same stained samples, we regard it as a useful character.

Heleopera petricola **Leidy 1879a** (Figure 23a)

H.petricola var. *amethystea* Penard 1899 can be separated on the basis of colour which is purple or violet. This is a valid criterion but we have only ever found a few individuals and these often occur with the uncoloured *H.petricola* so it may be a morphological variation of the same species. We include it under *H.petricola* here.

Other species included:

H.petricola var. *amethystea* Penard 1899

Dimensions: 75-85x50-60μm (this study), 56-150μm (Leidy, 1879a), 95-100μm (Penard, 1902), 60-73x40-57μm (Hoogenraad and de Groot, 1940), 56-65x39-46μm (Ogden and Hedley, 1980), 90-106x52-70μm (de Graaf, 1956), 70-135μm (Grospietsch, 1958), 80-125μm (Corbet, 1973), 75-95μm (Ellison and Ogden, 1987).

Test outline: ovoid in broad lateral view; flattened in narrow lateral view.

Colour: colourless but variable; brown, purple or violet.

Test material: siliceous plates with quartz particles in aboral region.

Aperture: terminal; 31-34μm diameter; aperture margins thickened, slightly convex; elliptical opening bordered by organic cement (Ogden and Hedley, 1980).

Other features: Corbet (1973) notes that *H. petricola* varies in size and colour, but that the aperture features separate *H. petricola* from the other species of *Heleopera*, except *H. rosea*, which can be distinguished by its colour (see below).

Heleopera rosea **Penard 1890** (Figure 23c)

Synonymy:

Heleopera lata Cash and Hopkinson 1909

Dimensions: 110-130x95-110μm (this study), 82-115x63-95μm (Hoogenraad and de Groot, 1956), 95-130μm (Grospietsch, 1958), 120-135μm (Corbet, 1973), 117-128x94-107μm (Ogden and Hedley, 1980), 110-125μm (Ellison and Ogden, 1987).

Test outline: ovoid in broad lateral view; flattened in narrow lateral view.

Colour: various shades of red. Wine red/rose red.

Test material: siliceous plates with some quartz particles in aboral region.

Aperture: terminal; thin linear slit (Ogden and Hedley, 1980); 47-73μm diameter.

Other features: distinguished from other members of Heleopera by colour. *H.lata* is described by Cash and Hopkinson (1909) as a distinct species on the basis of straighter sides and a broader aboral curve but we have included it under *H.rosea* as it shares the same colouration.

Heleopera sphagni **(Leidy 1874) Cash and Hopkinson 1909** (Figure 23d)

Synonymy:

Difflugia sphagni Leidy 1874

Heleopera picta Leidy 1879a

Dimensions: 90-120x70-75μm (this study), 80-130μm (Grospietsch, 1958), 100-145μm (Corbet, 1973), 94-108x70-73μm (Ogden and Hedley, 1980), 90-140μm (Ellison and Ogden, 1987).

Test outline: ovoid in broad lateral view; compressed in narrow lateral view.

Colour: golden yellow or brown.

Test material: siliceous plates at the apertural region; sand grains coating the aboral region.

Aperture: terminal; slightly convex in lateral view. Narrow and bordered by a thin collar of organic cement (Ogden and Hedley, 1980).

Heleopera sylvatica **Penard 1890** (Figure 23b)

Dimensions: 58-67μm (this study), 50-75μm but generally 60μm (Penard, 1902), breadth 25-30μm (Cash and Hopkinson, 1909).

Test outline: narrower and smaller than other members of *Heleopera*, sometimes with markedly convex apertural region.

Colour: colourless, transparent.

Test material: small quartz particles.

Aperture: terminal; strongly convex, curves smoothly round to side walls.

Hyalosphenia

This genus is characterised by tests which are entirely composed of secretion and therefore appear clear with smooth walls under the microscope. Confusion between species is

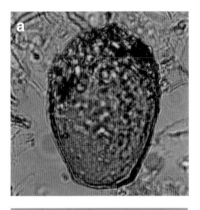

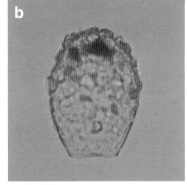

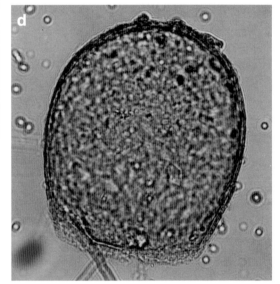

Figure 23:
a) *Heleopera petricola.*
b) *Heleopera sylvatica.*
c) *Heleopera rosea.*
d) *Heleopera sphagni.*

unlikely. Some rare individuals of *H. ovalis* have been observed with scattered small plates within a predominately secreted test and these appear to be intermediate between *H. ovalis* and *Nebela parvula*. However, this is extremely unusual and there is normally no confusion. The monograph by Grospietsch (1965) is useful for further detail.

Hyalosphenia elegans **Leidy (1874) 1875** (Figure 24a)

Synonymy:

Difflugia elegans Leidy 1874

Hyalosphenia elegans Leidy 1875

Dimensions: 81-96µm (this study), 90-100µm (Grospietsch, 1958; Corbet, 1973), 80µm (Ellison and Ogden, 1987), 80-94x35-47µm (Ogden, 1984).

Test outline: pyriform with distinct neck and surface undulations; compressed in narrow lateral view.

Colour: colourless to pale yellow.

Test material: proteinaceous.

Aperture: terminal, compressed.

Hyalosphenia ovalis **Wailes 1912b** (Figure 24c)

Synonymy:

? Hyalosphenia cuneata von Stein 1857

H. ovalis and *H. papilio* may be confused but are distinguished by the shape of the test which is oval and tapers convexly to the mouth in *H. ovalis* but is straight sided in *H. papilio*. However, by this criterion, a type slide of *H. ovalis* from the Penard collection at the British Museum would be identified as *H. papilio* and Cash *et al.* (1919) suggest that although the pyriform shape is the main reliable character, *H. papilio* may also tend towards this on occasion. However, we believe this is a reasonable separation even if it does not exactly concur with some early identifications. Wailes (1912b) also used larger size as a criterion to distinguish *H. ovalis* but this does not seem to be reliable. The drawing of *Hyalosphenia cuneata* von Stein 1857 in Cash and Hopkinson (1909) appears very similar to *H. ovalis* as defined here and would only be separated on the basis of size.

Dimensions: 34-41x25-32µm (this study), 153-177x130-140µm (Wailes, 1912b), 39x27µm (Warner, 1990).

Test outline: ovoid in broad lateral view; semi-circular aboral region; walls curve towards aperture.

Colour: colourless, transparent.

Test material: proteinaceous.

Aperture: terminal; straight, with smooth margins.

Hyalosphenia papilio **Leidy (1874) 1875** (Figure 24d)

Synonymy:

Difflugia papilio Leidy 1874

Hyalosphenia papilio Leidy 1875

Dimensions: 110-133x80-90μm (this study), 120x70μm (Hoogenraad and de Groot, 1940), 90-123x60-81μm (de Graaf, 1956), 90-130μm (Grospietsch, 1958; Corbet, 1973), 111-113x81-91μm (Ogden and Hedley, 1980), 150μm (Ellison and Ogden, 1980).

Test outline: ovoid with straight sided walls tapering uniformly to mouth in broad lateral view and strongly compressed in narrow lateral view.

Colour: pink-brown to colourless.

Test material: proteinaceous.

Aperture: terminal, 31-40μm.

Other features: one lateral pore present on each side at the widest part of the test. Ogden and Hedley (1980, after Grospietsch, 1965) note a second form of this species which has a concave aperture and several lateral pores.

Hyalosphenia subflava **Cash and Hopkinson 1909** (Figure 24b)

Synonymy:

Cash and Hopkinson describe a smaller species (*Hyalosphenia minuta* Cash 1891) but this would be included within our *H. subflava*.

Dimensions: 50-60x35-38μm (this study), 47-103x53-60μm (Hoogenraad and de Groot, 1940), 57-70μm (Grospietsch, 1958), 56-62x37-38μm (Ogden and Hedley, 1980).

Test outline: ovoid and smooth in broad lateral view; elliptical in narrow lateral view. Often distorted with iregular variations on this typical outline.

Colour: colourless or yellow.

Test material: proteinaceous.

Aperture: terminal, circular.

Other features: pores sometimes evident around the aperture.

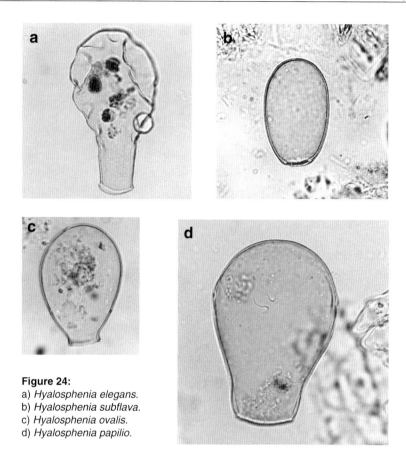

Figure 24:
a) *Hyalosphenia elegans.*
b) *Hyalosphenia subflava.*
c) *Hyalosphenia ovalis.*
d) *Hyalosphenia papilio.*

Lesquereusia spiralis **(Ehrenberg 1840) Bütschli 1880** (Figure 25)

The curved siliceous rods and shape of the neck render this a very distinctive species. Other species are *L. modesta* Rhumbler 1895 and *L. epistomium* Penard 1902. *L.modesta* is distinguished by sand grains rather than the siliceous rods of *L. spiralis*, and was reported from fen *Sphagnum* by Corbet (1973). *L. epistomium* has a more globose body and different neck angle (Cash and Hopkinson, 1909). However, we have only found typical *L. spiralis*.

Synonymy:

Difflugia spiralis Ehrenberg 1840

Lecquereusia spiralis Bütschli 1880

Dimensions: 90-120x85-110μm (this study), 100-150μm (Grospietsch, 1958), 89-117x86-109μm (Ogden and Hedley, 1980), 90-120μm (Ellison and Ogden, 1987).

Test outline: circular or ovoid in broad lateral view, with unsymmetrical neck. Compressed in narrow lateral view.

Colour: colourless.

Test material: siliceous rods interspersed with organic cement (Ogden and Hedley, 1980).

Aperture: terminal, circular and bordered by siliceous rods.

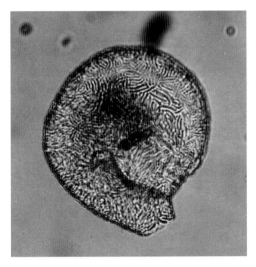

Figure 25: *Lesquereusia spiralis.*

Nebela

This is a large genus and many of the taxa are found in oligotrophic peatlands. However, most taxa are quite well defined and there is unlikely to be much confusion over most characters. Several taxa are separated by the presence or absence of small lateral pores. While these are often easy to see, they can be hard to discern if the test is not in a broad lateral view and can only be identified by carefully focusing up and down on the test wall, when the pores appear as small circular illuminated spots of light. Key references are Deflandre (1936) and Decloitre (1977a). *Nebela galeata* Penard 1890 is mentioned in the key but was not found by us and has not been included in the descriptions below. The compressed margin not forming a keel as in *N.carinata* and *N.marginata*, seems a clear character. Likewise *N. bigibbosa* Penard 1890 is referred to in the key as the character of two large pores on the broad face of the test is unmistakable although we have not found it in our work. See Deflandre (1936) for further descriptions of these and related species.

Nebela barbata **Leidy (1874) 1876b**

This is an extremely rare taxon and we have only found a few poorly preserved individuals. It is not illustrated here.

Synonymy:

Difflugia (Nebela) barbata Leidy 1874

Dimensions: 96-106x38-44μm (this study), 95-108x38μm (Hoogenraad and de Groot, 1940), 120-148x40-62μm (de Graaf, 1956), 80-160μm (Corbet, 1973), 96-106x38-44μm (Ogden and Hedley, 1980), 120-150μm (Ellison and Ogden, 1987).

Test outline: pyriform, with an elongated neck in broad lateral view.

Colour: colourless.

Test material: a mixture of oval, circular and elongate plates, with fine spines projecting from junctions of shell plates (Ogden and Hedley, 1980).

Aperture: terminal; oval and surrounded by a collar of organic cement. Ogden and Hedley (1980), using SEM, describe 8 tooth-like protrusions on the inner rim.

Other features: spines often flattened against the broad test surface and difficult to see. Ogden and Hedley (1980) note that the spines are fragile and may be lost in handling.

Nebela carinata **(Archer 1867) Leidy 1876b** (Figure 26a)

The separation of *N.carinata* and *N.marginata* may not always be clear (Bobrov, pers. comm.).

Synonymy:

Difflugia carinata Archer 1867

Nebela spumosa Awerintzew 1907

Dimensions: 140-200x110-152μm (this study), 197-240x150-173μm (Hoogenraad and de Groot, 1940), 170-22x125-140μm (de Graaf, 1956), 167-230μm (Grospietsch, 1958), 140-180μm (Corbet, 1973), 155-202x110-152μm (Ogden and Hedley, 1980), 160μm (Ellison and Ogden, 1987).

Test outline: oval or pyriform, with a compressed lateral margin which forms a broad keel extending to the aperture in broad lateral view. Flattened with compressed margins in narrow lateral view.

Colour: colourless.

Test material: composed of siliceous plates. Ogden and Hedley (1980) report that small beads of organic cement are often interspersed with the plates, but these are difficult to see under light microscopy.

Aperture: terminal, oval and surrounded by a thin collar of organic cement.

Other features: Ogden and Hedley (1980) note a small lateral pore at each margin.

Nebela collaris **(Ehrenberg 1848) Leidy 1879b** (Figure 27a)

Synonymy:

N.bohemica Taranek 1882

Difflugia collaris Ehrenberg 1848

Dimensions: 107-184μm (this study), 93-128x62-100μm (de Graaf, 1956), 94-184μm (Grospietsch, 1958), 107-184μm (Corbet, 1973), 98-153x72-91μm (Ogden and Hedley, 1980), 100-150μm (Ellison and Ogden, 1987).

Test outline: ovoid in broad lateral view, compressed in narrow lateral view.

Colour: colourless.

Test material: siliceous plates.

Aperture: terminal, ovoid, smooth thin collar of organic cement.

Nebela flabellulum **Leidy (1874) 1876b** (Figure 27e)

N.acolla Cash and Hopkinson 1909 has been separated on the basis of the lack of any sign of a neck. We include these forms under *N. flabellulum*.

Synonymy:

Difflugia (Nebela) flabellulum Leidy 1874

Nebela acolla Cash and Hopkinson 1909

Dimensions: 76-150x86-160μm (this study), 73-100x80-113μm (Hoogenraad and de Groot, 1940), 72-96μm (Corbet, 1973), 76-88x86-95μm (Ogden and Hedley, 1980), 100μm (Ellison and Ogden, 1987).

Test outline: circular or ovoid in broad lateral view, compressed in narrow lateral view.

Colour: colourless.

Test material: siliceous plates of assorted shapes and sizes. The plate edges are sometimes unclear, Ogden and Hedley (1980) ascribe this to a thin covering of organic cement.

Aperture: terminal; straight; oval; surrounded by a collar of organic cement. Diameter 18-25µm (Ogden and Hedley, 1980).

Nebela griseola **Penard 1911 type** (Figure 26b)

N.tenella Penard 1893 can be separated by a flattened test according to Deflandre (1936) but this is often difficult to determine, especially in fossil material.

Other species included:

N.tenella Penard 1893

Dimensions: 81-86x63-80µm (this study), 70-85µm (Deflandre, 1936), 67-97µm (Grospietsch, 1958), 70-85µm (Corbet, 1973), 82-88x62-69µm (Ogden and Hedley, 1980), 60-100µm (Ellison and Ogden, 1987).

Test outline: pyriform in broad lateral view; in narrow lateral view, slightly compressed.

Colour: yellow or brown greyish and opaque.

Test material: siliceous plates and quartz particles.

Aperture: terminal; circular and bordered by a prominent collar of plates. Diameter 20-21µm (Ogden and Hedley, 1980). Mouth recurved outwards to form a distinct lip (Corbet, 1973).

Nebela lageniformis **Penard 1890**

Smaller forms of this species have been described as another species, *N. wailesi* Deflandre 1936 (75-100 x 52-58µm, Deflandre,1936), but this has not been encountered here although it is common in New Zealand (Charman, 1997). Hoogenraad and de Groot (1940) give dimensions for *N.lageniformis* of 53-67x27-33µm but this is referable to *N.wailesi*.

Dimensions: 120-130µm (this study; Corbet 1973), 119-131µm (de Graaf, 1956), 119-131x68-85µm (Meisterfeld, 1979), 120µm (Ellison and Ogden, 1987).

Test outline: flask-shaped in broad lateral view; compressed in narrow lateral view.

Colour: colourless, transparent. Yellow-tinted (Corbet, 1973).

Test material: rounded siliceous plates cemented into neat rows.

Aperture: slightly convex with a thin border of secretion to produce a smooth rim.

Nebela marginata Penard 1902 (not illustrated)

Synonymy:

May include *N. maxima* Awerintzew 1907 although this is very much larger as described in Deflandre (1936).

Dimensions: 126-150x89-110µm (de Graaf, 1956), 140-170µm (Grospietsch, 1958; Corbet, 1973; Ellison and Ogden, 1987).

Test outline: pyriform in broad lateral view with thin compression at margins to produce a narrow keel; compressed in narrow lateral view.

Colour: tinted yellow-grey; brown (Corbet, 1973).

Test material: siliceous plates, bound by organic cement. Neatly arranged without touching each other.

Aperture: terminal; slightly concave, with a thin rim of secretion.

Other features: this species closely resembles *N. carinata* but can be distinguished by a narrower and shorter keel, which extends for half-distance along the test margins.

Nebela militaris Penard 1890 (Figure 27d)

The pores on this species can be difficult to discern so that this is not always a reliable character. In addition pores are sometimes reported from *N. minor*. Hence, small specimens of *N. minor* and large specimens of *N. militaris* may be confused, although this has rarely proved to be a problem in practice, since *N. militaris* is often much smaller (typically 50µm). For practical purposes then, all small Nebelids of this shape found in oligotrophic mires can be considered *N.militaris*.

Dimensions: 47-68x22-26µm (this study), 50-72x25-38µm (Deflandre, 1936), 59-70x33-41µm (Ogden and Hedley, 1980), 45-75µm (Ellison and Ogden, 1987), 29x15µm (Warner, 1990), 42-46x24-28µm (Bobrov *et al.*, 1995).

Test outline: pyriform or ovoid in broad lateral view; compressed in narrow lateral view. Lateral pores positioned near the aperture.

Colour: colourless.

Test material: mixture of circular, oval and circular siliceous plates.

Aperture: terminal, convex in broad lateral view. Diameter 10µm (this study), 15-18 (Ogden and Hedley, 1980), 12µm (Bobrov *et al.*, 1995). Narrow slit in transverse section. Surrounded by a thick organic collar.

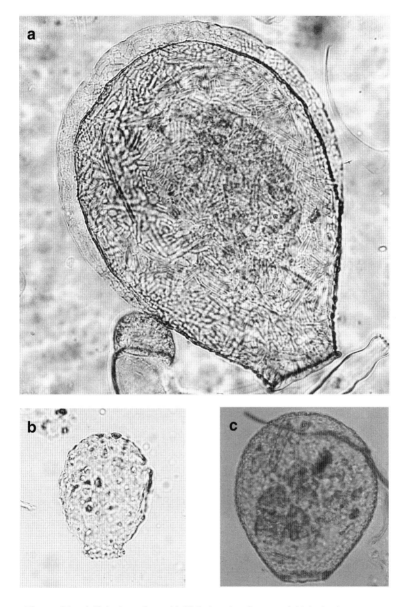

Figure 26: a) *Nebela carinata*. b) *Nebela griseola* type. c) *Nebela vitraea* type.

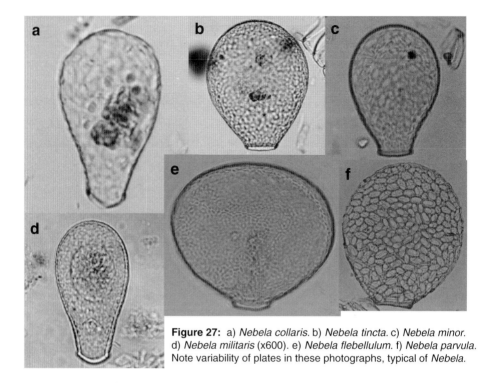

Figure 27: a) *Nebela collaris.* b) *Nebela tincta.* c) *Nebela minor.* d) *Nebela militaris* (x600). e) *Nebela flebellulum.* f) *Nebela parvula.* Note variability of plates in these photographs, typical of *Nebela.*

Nebela minor **Penard 1893** (Figure 27c)

Dimensions: 83-89μm (this study), 70-84x45-53μm (de Graaf, 1956), 90-100μm (Penard, 1902), 80-90μm (Wailes, 1912a), 85-94 x 53-62μm (Deflandre, 1936).

Test outline: pyriform; tapers to a wide aperture in broad lateral view. Lateral pores immediately behind aperture.

Colour: colourless; transparent.

Test material: elongate siliceous plates neatly cemented together.

Aperture: terminal, wide (23-27μm), with a thin border of organic cement.

Nebela parvula **Cash and Hopkinson 1909** (Figure 27f)

The distinction between *N. parvula* and *N. tincta* is based on the absence/presence of pores. This may result in misidentification of *N. tincta* as *N. parvula* where pores are hard to see.

Dimensions: 82-88μm (this study), 78-90μm (Grospietsch, 1958; Corbet, 1973)

Test outline: ovoid in broad lateral view, tapering to a straight aperture; compressed in narrow lateral view.

Colour: colourless and slightly transparent.

Test material: polygonal siliceous plates, irregularly cemented together.

Aperture: terminal, straight, with thin border of secretion.

Other features: very similar to *N. tincta*, but separated by absence of lateral pores, more transparent test and less pyriform outline (Corbet, 1973).

Nebela tincta **(Leidy 1879a) Awerintzew 1906** (Figure 27b)

Synonymy:

Hyalosphenia tincta Leidy 1879a

Dimensions: 78-89x54-67μm (this study), 80-110x54-83μm (de Graaf, 1956), 76-92μm (Grospietsch, 1958), 70-120μm (Corbet, 1973), 76-94x51-71μm (Ogden and Hedley, 1980).

Test outline: ovoid, with a small neck at the aperture in broad lateral view; compressed in narrow lateral view.

Colour: colourless and transparent, yellow (Ogden and Hedley, 1980).

Test material: oval or circular siliceous plates, obscured by a thin layer of organic cement (Ogden and Hedley, 1980).

Aperture: terminal, oval and surrounded by a thin collar.

Other features: a pair of small lateral pores located behind the aperture.

Nebela tubulosa **Penard 1890 type** (Figure 28)

There are several larger *Nebela* species with pyriform outlines with faint pores which are grouped here under *N. tubulosa* Penard 1890. *N. americana* Taranek 1882 was renamed by Deflandre as *N. penardiana* Deflandre 1936 and separated from *N. tubulosa* on the basis of small differences in plate structure. These are not always visible in sub-fossil specimens and the distinction cannot be made reliably. *N. speciosa* Deflandre 1936 is another related species differentiated primarily by size. We have not encountered enough specimens to be clear on the variability within this group, but suspect that size varies considerably although there is a clear break between this group and *N. militaris* which is similar in shape and possession of pores.

Synonymy:

N. americana Taranek 1882

N. speciosa Deflandre 1936

Nebela penardiana Deflandre 1936

Dimensions: 190-198x134-139µm (this study), 190-215x80-125µm (Penard, 1902), 213-264x120-155µm (Ogden and Hedley, 1980), 200-250µm (Ellison and Ogden, 1987).

Test outline: elongate, pyriform or ovoid with a distinct neck in broad lateral view, compressed in narrow lateral view. Lateral margin extends from base of neck and surrounds test.

Colour: yellow or brown.

Test material: oval and circular plates, untidily arranged and overlapping.

Aperture: terminal, oval, bordered by thin collar of organic cement (Ogden and Hedley, 1980). Diameter 42-54µm (Ogden and Hedley, 1980), 35-63µm (Penard, 1902).

Nebela vitraea **Penard 1899 type** (Figure 26c)

N. dentistoma Penard 1890 and *N. scotica* Brown 1911 are related species which are separated on the basis of the difference in plate structure and size of plates edging the mouth. All the specimens in our samples conformed to *N. vitraea* but it is possible that both of these other species were included. The plate structure is not always clear and the distinction between *N. dentistoma* and *N. scotica* by apertural plate size seems a little vague.

Other species included:

N. dentistoma Penard 1890

N. scotica Brown 1911

Dimensions: 120-151x104-138µm (this study), 155-258x120-140µm (Grospietsch, 1958), 95-231µm (Corbet, 1973), 117-160x102-145µm (Ogden and Hedley, 1980), 115-160µm (Ellison and Ogden, 1987).

Test outline: ovoid in broad lateral view, compressed in narrow lateral view.

Colour: colourless, glassy, clear yellow (Corbet, 1973).

Test material: mixture of oval and circular siliceous plates which overlap.

Aperture: terminal, surrounded by a border of plates, diameter 28-37µm (Ogden and Hedley, 1980).

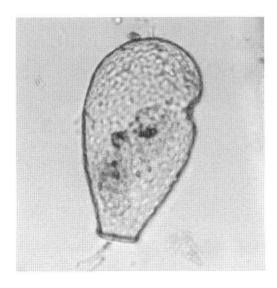

Figure 28: *Nebela tubulosa* type. Shown x100 as this a very large taxon.

Quadrulella

There are several species of *Quadrulella* and *Paraquadrula* which have been described. Cash and Hopkinson (1909) describe the species under the old name of *Quadrula symmetrica* and separate it from a smaller, more ovoid form called *Quadrula irregularis* Archer 1877. This appears to be the same as *Paraquadrula irregularis* described by Grospietsch (1958) differentiated by the plates which do not decrease in size towards the aperture. Deflandre (1936) grouped *Quadrulella* as a sub-genus of *Nebela*. Although we have encountered this species only rarely and always in more nutrient rich sites, all the individuals have conformed in shape, plates and size to the descriptions of *Quadrulella symmetrica*.

Quadrulella symmetrica (**Wallich 1863**) **Schulze 1875** (Figure 29)
Synonymy:
Difflugia protaeiformis var. *symmetrica* Wallich 1863
Quadrula symmetrica Schulze 1875
Nebela (Quadrulella) symmetrica Cockerell 1911

Dimensions: 80x41µm (this study), 68-120µm (Grospietsch, 1958; Corbet, 1973), 72-103x36-62µm (Ogden and Hedley, 1980), 70-110µm (Ellison and Ogden, 1987).

Test outline: ovoid or pyriform in broad lateral view; compressed in narrow lateral view.

Colour: colourless.

Test material: four-sided siliceous plates, arranged in regular rows, smaller plates closer to the aperture.

Aperture: terminal, oval, convex in broad lateral view, surrounded by a thin layer of organic cement.

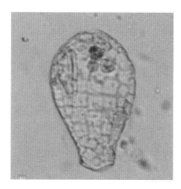

Figure 29: *Quadrulella symmetrica.*

8. PLAGIOPYXIDAE

The tests of this group are circular or ovoid and are almost spherical in three dimensions which can make them superficially similar to the Trigonopyxidae and the Centropyxidae. The tests are composed of mineral and organic particles and are often very darkly coloured which can make the individual xenosomes difficult to discern. The colouration can also obscure the aperture, which is subterminal and elongate. There are two genera (*Plagiopyxis* and *Bullinularia*) included but only *Bullinularia* has been recorded by us.

Bullinularia indica Penard 1907(Figure 30)

Distinguished from *Plagiopyxis* by the shape of the aperture which is a sickle shaped slit in *Plagiopyxis* but is straight in *Bullinularia*. Originally named *Bulinella indica* by Penard 1907 then renamed *Bullinula indica* by Penard (1911) and recently referred to as

Bullinularia indica (Grospietsch, 1958; Corbet, 1973; Tolonen, 1986) although it is not clear on what basis. We use the latter genus name as it is in common use. *Bullinula minor* Hoogenraad and de Groot 1948 was distinguished by its smaller size but only a few specimens from a single sample were examined.

Synonymy:

Bulinella indica Penard 1907

Bullinula indica Penard 1911

Bullinula minor Hoogenraad and de Groot 1948

Dimensions: diameter 140-150µm (this study), diameter 160-170µm (de Graaf, 1956), diameter 150-220µm (Grospietsch, 1958; Corbet, 1973), diameter 138-148µm (Ogden and Hedley, 1980), diameter 120-200µm (Ellison and Ogden, 1987).

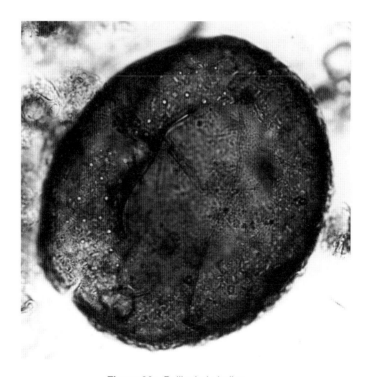

Figure 30: *Bullinularia indica.*

Test outline: oval or circular in broad lateral view, hemispherical or spherical in narrow lateral view.

Colour: dark brown.

Test material: mineral particles cemented together to produce a rough surface.

Aperture: sub-terminal, narrow, elongate slit, inner lip depressed, outer lip invaginated (Ogden and Hedley, 1980). Length 66-69μm (this study), 65-69μm (Ogden and Hedley, 1980).

9. TRINEMATIIDAE: Two genera: *Trinema* and *Corythion*

This is a difficult group to provide adequate taxon definitions for. The tests are often rather delicate with thin walls and fine plates which are difficult to see, especially in fossil specimens. The tests are ovoid, composed of circular siliceous plates, and the aperture is sub-terminal. The two genera are separated according to whether the plates touch each other (*Trinema*) or are interspersed by organic cement (*Corythion*), but since the plates are often difficult to see, this is not an easy character to apply (Corbet, 1973). *Trinema* species also usually have larger circular plates whereas *Corythion* has smaller, elongated plates arranged more irregularly. In our work *Trinema lineare* Penard 1890 is separated by its smaller size, apparent absence of plates and its unflattened shape. *Corythion dubium* Taranek 1881 and *Trinema enchelys* Leidy 1878 are combined into a single taxon here due to the small size of the test and transparent plates, following Corbet (1973). It is likely that this also includes *T. complanatum* Penard 1890 and *T. penardi* Thomas and Chardez 1958. Lüftenegger *et al.* (1988) provide some useful additional descriptions, diagrams and photographs of these species with biometric data. Although it may be possible separate some of these species given well preserved individuals and careful recording of all dimensions, it would not be possible to do this consistently for most fossil specimens. In addition, Table 8 shows that some of the size ranges for *Trinema-Corythion* type overlap but most authors except Lüftenegger *et al.* (1988) report sizes of *T. lineare* below 30μm. The characters used here seem to work well in most cases although there may be some misidentification of specimens in the range 25-35μm.

Corythion-Trinema **type** (Figure 31a)

Other species included:

Corythion dubium Taranek 1881

Trinema enchelys Leidy 1878
T.complanatum Penard 1890
T.penardi Thomas and Chardez 1958
Dimensions: see Table 8.
Test outline: elongate, ovoid test in broad lateral view; compressed in narrow lateral view.
Test material: all species have siliceous plates. In *C. dubium* the plates are small sub-rectangular to oval and irregularly arranged; in *T. enchelys* they are circular and regularly arranged.
Aperture: sub-terminal and circular or ovoid; invaginated.

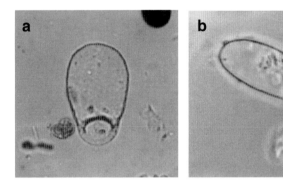

Figure 31: a) *Corythion-Trinema* type broad lateral view.
b) *Trinema lineare* narrow lateral view (x1000).

Trinema lineare **Penard 1890** (Figure 31b)
Dimensions: See Table 8.
Test outline: elongate, ovoid test in broad lateral view; compressed in narrow lateral view.
Colour: colourless; appears transparent.
Test material: oval or circular siliceous plates, usually impossible to see under light microscopy.
Aperture: sub-terminal; circular; invaginated. 3-6µm (Decloitre, 1981).
Other features: Bobrov *et al.* (1999) separate this taxon into three separate taxa but there are no differences between them in terms of habitat preferences and it is probably

not easy to do this consistently in fossil specimens. *Trinema lineare* var. *truncatum* Chardez 1964 has a pseudostome at right angles to the test length (Chardez 1964) whereas *Trinema lineare* var. *terricola* Decloitre 1962b and *T. lineare* Penard 1890 have oblique pseudostomes, with a more extreme angle in *T. lineare* var. *terricola*.

Species	Length	Breadth	Aperture
Corythion dubium Taranek 1881	30-60	26-62	18-41
Trinema enchelys Leidy 1878	32-103	15-60	7-11
T.complanatum Penard 1890	24-75	13-45	6.5-16
T.penardi Thomas and Chardez 1958	30-65	16-35	5-15
T.lineare Penard 1890	16-41	7-19	1.2-10

Table 8: Dimensions (μm) of species within the *Trinema-Corythion* type and for *T.lineare*. Data taken from Lüftenegger *et al.* (1988) and Decloitre (1981), which together contain the largest range of variation reported for the species, except for apertural diameter of *T.lineare* taken from Ogden and Hedley (1980).

CHAPTER 6.
HYDROLOGICAL INDICATOR VALUES AND DATA
ANALYSIS

The principal ecological factors that affect assemblage composition were reviewed in Chapter 2. All previous work on peatlands shows that hydrology is the principal control on species composition and since reconstruction of surface wetness conditions is most often the subject of peatland studies, this is the focus of this chapter. However, testate amoebae may also be used as indicators of pH changes in some circumstances and this is an area with some promise for the future (e.g. Mitchell *et al.*, 2001), but based on similar data analysis methods to those considered here. The main aim of this chapter is to review approaches to the hydrological interpretation of testate amoebae assemblages with an emphasis on the application of quantitative approaches which have been applied over the past decade and which have become increasingly accessible and easy to use in recent years. A principal aid to the interpretation of fossil faunas is provided by summary tables of known ecological indicator values from previous studies (Tables 9 and 10).

The chapter is thus presented in three parts: ecological indicator values, qualitative reconstructions and quantitative reconstructions. Both qualitative and quantitative approaches ultimately depend on an adequate knowledge of the modern ecology of testate amoebae and this is an area where much work has been done over the past 10-15 years. Much of this ecological work has been quantitative itself but the results may also be used subjectively to produce qualitative reconstructions of past conditions. In deciding whether to attempt quantitative reconstructions of hydrological conditions, the quality of the modern data must be carefully considered. For example, while close similarities may exist between taxa-environment relationships in different geographical areas (see Chapter 2, Table 4), it would be unreasonable to use data from one region to directly infer conditions about another area, for example with a transfer function approach. Numerical estimates of hydrological conditions may initially seem more attractive but if they are based on unreliable data they may be highly misleading. Thus data evaluation and error estimation are important parts of the choice and application of appropriate reconstruction techniques. The second part of the chapter considers essentially qualitative approaches which use ecological data in a subjective way to infer past conditions, perhaps interpreting fossil assemblages as reflecting a variety of conditions on a descriptive scale from very wet to very dry. The third part reviews approaches that attempt to use the relationship between hydrology and modern assemblages to establish quantitative reconstructions of past hydrological changes.

6.1 Hydrological indicator values of testate amoebae

The terminology for surface wetness conditions affecting testate amoebae was described in Chapter 2 (see Table 3) and a variety of approaches have been used over the years. In addition to studies which have focussed on the assessment of hydrological preferences there are also references to typical habitats of some taxa in some of the early taxonomic work such as the four volumes of Cash *et al.* (1905-1918). While these early sources do not provide much detail they can be useful for rare taxa which have not been encountered in later ecological work. More recent studies use methods which result in quantitative estimates of the hydrological optima for different taxa. Two summary tables of hydrological indicator values are provided here as an aid to the interpretation of fossil faunas. Table 9 lists taxa alphabetically and summarises the known ecological niches in qualitative terms with reference to some of the more recent estimates for hydrological optima from individual studies. Table 10 reviews the published quantitative data on hydrological associations for specific regions expressed as depth to water table.

Recent work has concentrated on detailed ecological work and the collection of data sets which aim to provide quantitative data on habitat preferences. However, there has been rather little attempt to bring these together to begin to make comparisons between taxa over large geographical areas. The data in Tables 9 and 10 provide a basis for a first step towards this. The division between Table 10 a) and 10 b) is purely for convenience and although it is done principally on a geographical basis, it could equally be argued that one might expect to see greater similarity between continental and oceanic areas, especially in the northern hemisphere. These data should ideally be used to interpret fossil data from within the region from which they were collected but there will be many situations where no modern data area available and none can be gathered within the resources of what may be principally a 'palaeo' project. It is therefore useful to examine the data to begin to look for similarities and differences between geographic regions at this stage, with the aim of identifying taxa which appear to have rather similar indicator values wherever they occur. One of the difficulties which should be borne in mind when making such comparisons is that not all taxa occur in sufficient numbers in all regions studied to draw meaningful conclusions. Table 10 excludes taxa with less than five occurrences in a particular region but despite this may contain some misleading data. A further problem is that most water table optima are based on seasonal data from a single year only and although internally consistent, may not be comparable between regions.

There are a number of taxa which appear to have rather consistent indicator values across all the regions studied. Taxa from the genus *Arcella* often appear at the wetter end of sampled gradients. The commonest taxon *Arcella discoides* type, and where separated, *A. rotundata* var. *aplanata*, are consistent in this respect, even in the Southern Hemisphere data available (Charman, 1997). Some of the other commonly reported taxa are less consistent. *A. catinus* and *A. artocrea* both appear at variable positions on sampled hydrological gradients. Other wet indicators with relatively little variability between regions are *Amphitrema wrightianum* and *A. flavum*, with the former always occupying wetter sites than the latter. There appear to be significant differences in patterns of *Amphitrema* between extreme oceanic areas (UK and Newfoundland) and more continental regions. *A. flavum* is further down the gradient in oceanic conditions than *A. wrightianum*, and *A. stenostoma* is more common in oceanic conditions. In extreme continental areas (Minnesota, USA and Ontario, Canada), *A. wrightianum* is rare or completely absent. *Difflugia* taxa generally occur at intermediate to wet locations, some of the commonest taxa being *D. bacillifera, D. oblonga* and *D. leidyi*, the first two taxa also appearing in New Zealand as well as Northern Hemisphere regions.

There are a few common genera which are consistently found in drier locations with no species in wet locations. For example *Trigonopyxis arcula* is an easily recognised taxon in this category. The identification of taxa within the genera *Trinema* and *Corythion* is not so easy (see Chapter 5) but it could be argued that identification to the lowest taxonomic divisions is not necessary for hydrological interpretation since all taxa occur in drier locations. Where detailed separations have been made, there are differences between taxa but these are of a relatively small magnitude (Bobrov *et al.*, 1999). *Assulina* is probably the commonest genus in all studies and although the two main taxa, *A. muscorum* and *A. seminulum*, are found in a wide range of conditions, they are most abundant in intermediate to dry locations. Again, there is some consistent variation within the genus, with *A. seminulum* in wetter locations than *A. muscorum*. A closely related taxon not usually separated, *Valkanovia elegans*, may be an even drier indicator (Bobrov *et al.*, 1999). *Euglypha* taxa are generally drier indicators, although there are some exceptions to this. The commonest taxa recovered from peats are the spineless *E. rotunda* and *E. tuberculata* types, the former tending to occupy slightly drier positions than the latter but both taxa in the intermediate to dry end of the gradient. Spined forms are more variable in habitat preferences. *E. strigosa* is the most commonly reported but appears to be variable in its preferred niche. More detailed studies suggest that there may be much more complex patterns within *Euglypha* where efforts are made to separate taxa to lower levels (Bobrov *et al.*, 1999).

Some genera span almost the entire gradient in many data sets and allow comparisons of the relative hydrological ranking of particular taxa. For example in *Hyalosphenia, H. elegans* and *H. papilio* are both relatively wet indicators while *H. subflava* is consistently an extreme dry indicator, although there is some deviation from this pattern in Newfoundland (Charman and Warner, 1997). There are many taxa within the genus *Nebela*, but *N. carinata* and *N. marginata* are often the wettest taxa, with *N. militaris, N.*

parvula and *N. tincta* the commonest taxa at intermediate to dry positions. One taxon, . *flabellulum*, is notable as a very dry indicator reported only from oceanic areas (Charman and Warner, 1997; Woodland *et al.*, 1998). In the southern hemisphere, there are a different set of *Nebela* taxa which look as if they will be useful indicators of past hydrological conditions. However, the data are too few at present to be clear what the relationships are.

There are a number of taxa which are relatively common but for which no really clear patterns have emerged. The *Centropyxis-Cyclopyxis* group is a complex group which is most often only split into a few major forms, although many subtly different variations have been described (see Chapter 5). This may be one of the reasons why indicator values differ between regions for the group, although there is some suggestion that spined forms (principally *Centropyxis aculeata* type) occur in wetter locations than others in this group (Tolonen *et al.*, 1994; Woodland *et al.*, 1998; Mitchell *et al.*, 1999). *Heleopera* is another genus where patterns are hard to discern, and there seems to be a large amount of variability across different geographic regions. In this case, taxonomy is simpler so observed differences are likely to be real rather than affected by grouping or differences between observers.

In summary, there are now major patterns emerging from the increasing number of studies being carried out on the ecology of testate amoebae. While detailed comparisons can not yet really be drawn, given the variability in the measurement of water tables (i.e. difference between years and seasons), future work is likely to fine tune these comparisons to provide more definitive data. However, it is possible to gain a lot of information simply by using the kinds of observations made above to interpret a fossil assemblage in a purely subjective way. Major changes in assemblages are often easy to interpret in this way but more subtle variations in hydrology can be missed. The approaches described below can help in identifying these variations.

earch Association

in peats

7.

ιbetical list of taxa with summary of qualitative hydrological indicator values based
ervations from selected published sources and experience of the authors.

Comments on hydrological indicator value

Amphitrema flavum	Generally associated with wet conditions, sometimes with standing water (Meisterfeld, 1977; Tolonen 1966; Warner, 1987) but extends to hummock tops in oceanic areas (Heal, 1964)
Amphitrema stenostoma	A bog pool taxon, often with *A. wrightianum* (Corbet, 1973; Tolonen, 1986)
Amphitrema wrightianum	Bog pools and wet hollows but also in mesotrophic fen peats (Tolonen, 1986)
Arcella artrocrea	Moderately wet conditions
Arcella catinus type	Hygrophilous according to de Graaf (1956) but also on dry hummocks (Heal, 1961). One of the taxa included (*A. arenaria*) is regarded as xerophilous (Tolonen, 1986)
Arcella discoides type	Generally associated with very wet conditions, often with standing water. *A. rotunda* var *aplanata*, which we include in this taxon also occurs in submerged or very wet *Sphagnum* swards (Tolonen, 1986)
Arcella gibbosa type	Submerged *Sphagnum* (de Graaf, 1956)
Arcella hemispherica	Few data, but also recovered from minerotrophic conditions
Arcella vulgaris	Too few data, but most likely to be semi-aquatic as many other *Arcella*
Assulina muscorum	Widespread but generally in greatest abundance in relatively dry conditions (Tolonen, 1986), although it is often regarded as cosmopolitan (Warner, 1990)
Assulina seminulum	A hygrophilous taxon but also occurring in bog hummocks according to Corbet (1973)
Bullinularia indica	All authors regard this taxon as an extreme xerophile, in hummocks or forested peatland (e.g. Heal, 1961, 1964; de Graaf, 1956; Tolonen, 1986)

Centropyxis aculeata type   Mostly associated with aquatic habitats (de Graaf,1956; Schönborn, 1962) or very wet conditions (Warner, 1987)

Centropyxis cassis type   According to de Graaf (1956) this taxon is typical of hygrophilous, submerged & wet mosses. Tolonen (1986) suggest most of the taxa within this complex are hygrophilous

Centropyxis platystoma type   As above

Corythion-Trinema type   Variable conditions but most typical of dry or moderately dry conditions (de Graaf, 1956; Meisterfeld, 1977; Schönborn, 1962)

Cyclopyxis arcelloides type   Variable conditions from moderately dry (Warner,1987) to ponds, shallow peatland pools and very wet *Sphagnum* soils. Again complicated by being a complex, including *Phryganella acropodia*, noted as associated with dry mosses by Schönborn (1962)

Cryptodifflugia oviformis   Again, variable conditions are reported including saturated and submerged wet *Sphagnum* (Heal, 1964) to dry bog hummocks (Tolonen, 1966). Hedley *et al.* (1977) suggest it is cosmopolitan

Cryptodifflugia sacculus   Probably a relatively wet indicator (e.g. Charman and Warner, 1997)

Difflugia acuminata   A hydrophilous taxon found in bog pools (Cash & Hopkinson, 1909; de Graaf 1956)

Difflugia bacillariarum   A bog pool taxon (Corbet, 1973; Heal, 1961)

Difflugia bacillifera   All authors regard this as a hydrophilous taxon typically found in *Sphagnum* pools (Cash and Hopkinson, 1909; de Graaf, 1956; Corbet,1973)

Difflugia globulosa   Aquatic habitats (de Graaf, 1956)

Difflugia lanceolata   Bog pools (Cash and Hopkinson, 1909)

Difflugia leidyi   Wet conditions with >95% moisture content (Tolonen *et al.*, 1992)

Difflugia lucida type   Inadequate number of finds but most likely to be semi-aquatic

Difflugia oblonga type	Very wet *Sphagnum* (de Graaf, 1956)
Difflugia pristis type	Some taxa within this group are reported from very wet conditions (e.g. *D. angulostoma* is aquatic according to Cash and Hopkinson, 1909) and modern samples suggest that wet conditions (although not standing water) are typical (Woodland *et al.*, 1998)
Difflugia pulex	A rare taxon in modern studies with no published hydrological data available. On the basis of associations with other taxa in fossil samples, Hendon (1998) suggests it is a relatively dry indicator
Difflugia rubescens	Hydrophilous (de Graaf 1956) and often in wet hollows or shallow pools
Euglypha ciliata	Moderately wet conditions (Woodland *et al.*, 1998; Bobrov *et al.*, 1999)
Euglypha compressa	As with *E. ciliata*, this taxon is probably most characteristic of moderately wet conditions but has rarely been found in high enough abundance to be clear on this. Woodland *et al.* (1998) found it in the wettest conditions they sampled so it may be an aquatic taxon
Euglypha rotunda type	Reported from wet mosses and standing water by Hedley and Ogden (1973), but perhaps more typical of intermediate conditions
Euglypha strigosa	Sometimes regarded as a taxon of bog hummocks (Heal, 1961), but more often found in wet *Sphagnum* and even semi-aquatic conditions (e.g. Woodland *et al.*, 1998; Bobrov *et al.*, 1999)
Euglypha tuberculata type	Intermediate conditions but usually in wetter locations than *E. rotunda* type
Heleopera petricola	The ecology of this taxon appears to be variable and is disputed (Tolonen, 1986; Warner, 1987) with suggestions it is a wet taxon (a-hydrophilous, de Graaf, 1956) or more typical of bog hummocks (Heal, 1961, 1964)
Heleopera rosea	Bog hummocks and drier *Sphagnum* (Jung, 1936, quoted in Tolonen, 1986)

Heleopera sphagni	b-hygrophilous taxon (de Graaf 1956)
Heleopera sylvatica	Generally restricted to drier mosses and bog hummocks (Tolonen, 1986) and in drained mires (Tolonen *et al.*, 1992)
Hyalosphenia elegans	A hydrophilous taxon found in wet *Sphagnum,* although not usually in bog pools.a-hydrophilous according to de Graaf (1956)
Hyalosphenia ovalis	There is rather little published information on this taxon, but Tolonen (1986) suggests it is typical of raised bog pools and also wet minerotrophic habitats
Hyalosphenia papilio	Wet *Sphagnum* (de Graaf, 1956) including wetter hummocks (Heal, 1961) but not in pools or hollows
Hyalosphenia subflava	A dry indicator which has sometimes been regarded as only present in soils and drained peatlands (Tolonen, 1986; Warner, 1989). However, it is very common in mid-late Holocene peats in Britain. A reliable dry indicator
Lesquereusia spiralis	Uncommon but hydrophilous (de Graaf, 1956)
Nebela barbata	Hydrophilous (de Graaf, 1956)
Nebela carinata	Usually in very wet *Sphagnum* and often in pools (Heal, 1964)
Nebela collaris	Generally in moderately dry conditions (de Graaf, 1956), b-hygrophilous or moisture class V (Tolonen, 1986)
Nebela dentistoma	Quite rare but probably indicative of moderately wet conditions (e.g. Charman and Warner, 1997)
Nebela flabellulum	*Sphagnum* in bog hummocks (Corbet, 1973)
Nebela griseola type	Probably has quite a wide range. Tolonen (1986) suggests it is quite a hydrophilous taxon but Corbet (1973) describes it as a taxon of the *Sphagnum* on drier hummocks
Nebela lageniformis	Intermediate conditions, more common in minerotrophic situations
Nebela marginata	a-hygrophilous taxon (de Graaf 1956) in very wet conditions (Meisterfeld, 1977)

Nebela militaris	Most authors agree that *N. militaris* is a relatively dry indicator of drier mosses and bog hummocks (de Graaf, 1956; Corbet, 1973; Heal, 1961)
Nebela minor	Moderately wet conditions (typically *Sphagnum* lawns)
Nebela parvula	Like *N. tincta*, sometimes thought of as a dry indicator but also found in wetter situations so status is uncertain
Nebela tincta	Often regarded as a xerophilous taxon (Tolonen, 1986; Tolonen *et al.*, 1992) but also reported as occurring in 'very wet' conditions (Warner, 1987)
Nebela tubulosa type	Insufficient data
Placocista spinosa type	Typical of bog pools or very wet conditions (Corbet, 1973; Heal, 1961)
Plagiopyxis callida	Rarely found. Typical conditions unknown
Pseudodifflugia fascicularis	Described as 'aquatic' by Cash and Hopkinson (1909), but could be more variable and may be favoured by enriched conditions (Hendon, 1998)
Pseudodifflugia fulva type	Insufficient data
Quadrulella symmetrica	A species of wet and often enriched sites, most common on minerotrophic mires
Sphenoderia lenta	Sometimes regarded as a relatively wet taxon (a-hygrophilous in wet *Sphagna*, de Graaf, 1956) but also found in moderately dry conditions (Tolonen *et al.*, 1992; Warner, 1987; Warner, 1990)
Trigonopyxis arcula type	Universally regarded as a xerophilous taxon often at the very driest end of the hydrological gradient in ombrotrophic mires but also present in wetter minerotrophic conditions (Tolonen, 1986)
Trinema lineare	Usually on drier sites, but can be variable if confused with some taxa within *Corythion-Trinema* type

6.2 Qualitative interpretations

There are a variety of ways in which a basic understanding of the relationship between surface wetness and testate amoebae assemblages can be used in qualitative reconstructions from fossil data. These are divisible into four:

1. General subjective interpretation
2. Indicator species
3. Inferring wetness zones
4. Producing a semi-quantitative curve of wetness changes

The simplest approach is to use existing knowledge to inform the biostratigraphy of a profile, especially where there are other data also available. One of the best early examples of this approach is that of Tolonen (1966) in elucidating the main changes on a raised mire in Finland. Here the interpretation was based on the limited existing work as well as on a small number of surface samples from the same mire used for the fossil data. However, these data were relatively limited and interpretation was mostly based on a relatively small number of taxa for which the ecological conditions were relatively well known (especially *Amphitrema flavum*, *Trigonopyxis arcula* and *Hyalosphenia papilio*). This approach is still used to good effect in studies today, especially where hydrological trends over particular horizons are of key interest. Mauquoy and Barber (1999) found that even widely spaced samples showed clear hydrological trends over the period when *Sphagnum imbricatum* underwent its dramatic decline in the 12th to 15th centuries on a number of sites in northern England. Again in this case, fluctuations in key taxa were most useful (*Amphitrema flavum* and *A. wrightianum*, as wet indicators, *Trigonopyxis arcula* and *Hyalosphenia subflava* as dry indicators).

Well-known studies using only one or two indicators are those of Aaby (1976) and Aaby and Tauber (1975). Here, the abundance of *Amphitrema flavum* and *Assulina* (including *A. muscorum* and *A. seminulum*) were estimated by counts from pollen preparations and expression of the changes as a percentage of the arboreal pollen sum. While we would not recommend this approach now as it is too prone to being affected by slight differences in preparations (see Chapter 3), the results do agree with data based on peat humification changes. The fundamental difficulty with attempting to use only one or two

Table 10: Hydrological indicator values for taxa recorded in studies of peatlands worldwide, sorted by depth to water table (cm) a) Data from North America and New Zealand b) Data from Europe .

General notes:

1. All values are derived from weighted average estimates of optima for water tables (cm) at the time of sampling (normally during the summer season, except for the UK where mean annual values are used).
2. All taxa names are as given by original authors with some notes on taxa not referred to elsewhere in this guide. See original papers for further details.
3. Taxa with <5 occurrences are excluded.
4. Negative values refer to water tables above the surface.
5. Data given to two decimal places where available or otherwise as published data.

Table 10 a): Data from North America and New Zealand

Continental Canada/USA (Minnesota & NW Ontario) Warner and Charman (1994)		Continental Canada (NE Ontario) Charman and Warner (1992)		Oceanic Canada (Newfoundland) Charman and Warner (1997)		New Zealand[j] Charman (1997)	
Arcella hemisphaerica	2.8	Hyalosphenia papilio	23.13	Arcella discoides	0.91	A. rotundata v. aplanata[a]	1.99
Arcella rotundata var. aplanata[a]	4.4	Amphitrema flavum	24.69	Nebela carinata	1.09	Arcella discoides	2.92
Arcella discoides	9.0	Hyalosphenia elegans	25.86	Cryptodifflugia sacculus	1.42	Difflugia bacillifera	5.63
Arcella catinus	9.1	Heleopera sphagni	26.95	Difflugia bacillifera	2.19	Nebela vas[j]	6.57
Hyalosphenia papilio	9.9	Centropyxis aculeata	27.03	Amphitrema wrightianum	4.07	Difflugia oblonga	7.69
Difflugia oblonga	11.0	Nebela penardiana[g]	27.60	Cyclopyxis arcelloides	4.69	Difflugia sp (ABD)[j]	8.19
Amphitrema flavum	15.0	Nebela lageniformis	29.20	Centropyxis aerophila type[b]	5.16	Nebela certesi[j]	8.80
Centropyxis aerophylla[b]	20.5	Heleopera rosea	29.91	Difflugia oblonga	5.25	Pontigulasia spp	9.81
Sphenoderia lenta	22.4	Hyalosphenia ovalis	32.04	Sphenoderia lenta	5.86	Heleopera petricola	10.27
Heleopera sylvatica	23.4	Nebela militaris	32.10	Quadrulella symmetrica	6.00	Difflugia oblonga cf.	11.29
Centropyxis aculeata	24.3	Nebela parvula	32.29	Centropyxis aculeata type	6.18	Difflugia type C[j]	12.48
Hyalosphenia elegans	26.3	Coryhion spp[c]	32.81	Amphitrema stenostoma	6.54	Sphenoderia fissirostris	12.77
Nebela parvula	27.6	Heleopera petricola	33.39	Nebela marginata	6.89	Heleopera sylvatica	14.46
Heleopera petricola	31.1	Euglypha rotunda	33.58	Nebela parvula	6.98	Nebela wailesi	14.71
Cyclopyxis arcelloides	32.0	Cyclopyxis arcelloides	33.61	Heleopera petricola	7.27	Hyalosphenia subflava	14.94
Nebela tincta	32.6	Euglypha tuberculata	33.65	Placocista spinosa	7.44	Nebela tuberculata	15.50
Euglypha tuberculata	36.6	Sphenoderia lenta	33.71	Difflugia oviformis	7.47	Euglypha tuberculata	15.74
Euglypha rotunda	38.9	Assulina muscorum	33.87	Nebela dentistoma[l]	9.07	Nebela cockayni[j]	16.16
Assulina seminulum	39.3	Centropyxis aerophylla[b]	33.99	Nebela minor	9.33	Nebela parvula	16.83

Species	Value		Species	Value		Species	Value		Species	Value
Trinema spp.[c]	40.2		*Nebela tincta*	34.46		*Plagiopyxis callida*	9.40		*Corython dubium*	16.99
Nebela militaris	41.9		*Trinema* spp[c]	34.63		*Arcella catinus*	9.81		*Nebela caudata*[i]	17.36
Assulina muscorum	42.5		*Bullinaria indica*	34.83		*Amphitrema flavum*	10.27		*Centropyxis platystoma* type	17.92
Hyalosphenia ovalis	42.9		*Euglypha strigosa*[d]	34.87		*Nebela griseola*	11.14		*Centropyxis cassis* type	17.92
Heleopera sphagni	44.2		*Trigonopyxis arcula*	35.01		*Heleopera sphagni*	11.61		*Nebela tincta*	18.80
Euglypha strigosa[d]	45.6		*Cryptodifflugia sacculus*	35.10		*Nebela tincta*	11.67		*Nebela militaris*	19.09
Corython spp.[e]	47.5		*Assulina seminulum*	35.31		*Assulina seminulum*	13.95		*Euglypha rotunda*	20.14
Hyalosphenia subflava	49.9		*Nebela griseola*	35.82		*Euglypha tuberculata*	14.43		*Assulina muscorum*	20.61
Bullinaria indica	50.1		*Arcella artrocrea*[h]	35.87		*Trigonopyxis arcula*	15.58		*Phryganella acropodia* cf.	23.33
Phryganella acropodia[f]	52.8		*Hyalosphenia subflava*	36.22		*Assulina muscorum*	17.44		*Difflugia tuberculata*	24.60
Trigonopyxis arcula	57.7		*Plagiopyxis callida*	37.73		*Hyalosphenia papilio*	17.74		*Euglypha strigosa*	33.57
			Arcella catinus	38.83		*Nebela lagenformis*	18.01		*Cyclopyxis arcelloides* type	35.71
						Euglypha rotunda type	18.41			
						Hyalosphenia ovalis	19.96			
						Nebela militaris	20.66			
						Hyalosphenia elegans	21.59			
						Hyalosphenia subflava	22.81			
						Heleopera sylvatica	23.22			
						Corython type[e]	23.51			
						Nebela flabulellum	30.04			

Additional specific notes applicable to table 10 a) and 10 b):

1. Data from Charman and Warner (1992) are expressed as previously unpublished values of depth to water tables. In this case these may be less reliable than the published % soil moisture values as a number of measurements were noted as >41 cm and were not measured precisely. However, depth to water table is used here for comparability with other data.

2. Taxonomic notes (see species descriptions for further details of discussion of synonymy)
a. *Arcella rotundata* var.*aplanata* separated from *A. discoides* type on the basis of thickened rim to mouth
b. *Centropyxis aerophylla* and *C. aerophila* = *C. cassis* type
c. *Trinema* spp. = *Trinema lineare* type
d. *Euglypha strigosa* not separated here from other *Euglypha* taxa with spines and may therefore include *E. compressa* and *E. ciliata* types.
e. *Corython* spp., *Corython* type and *Corython dubium* type = *Corython-Trinema* type
f. *Phryganella acropodia* separated from *Cyclopyxis arcelloides* on the basis of organic detritus in test
g. *Nebela penardiana* = *Nebela tubulosa* type
h. *Arcella artrocrea* not differentiated from *A. gibbosa*
i. The differentiation between *Nebela dentistoma* and *N. vitraea* is not always straightforward and there may be overlap between these taxa.
j. There are a number of taxa in the southern hemisphere which do not appear at all in northern sites. This guide does not include these at present. All nomenclature for the New Zealand sites is based on the same criteria as are described here, with the exception of these taxa.

Table 10 b): Data from Europe

United Kingdom (Woodland et al. (1998))		Jura Mountains (Mitchell et al. (2001))		Finland (Tolonen et al. (1994))		Western Russia[1] (Bobrov et al. (1999))	
1.89	Euglypha compressa	Nebela marginata	9	0.8	Amphitrema wrightianum	Arcella rotundata var. aplanata	-4.0
2.03	Arcella hemispherica	Amphitrema wrightianum	9	1.4	Nebela carinata	Nebela marginata	-3.4
3.23	Nebela lageniformis	Nebela carinata	10	2.3	Difflugia leidyi	Difflugia bacillariarum	-2.0
3.33	Arcella discoides	Amphitrema flavum	11	2.8	Amphitrema flavum	Difflugia bacillifera	-1.9
3.52	Amphitrema wrightianum	Arcella artocrea	14	3.1	Heleopera petricola	Difflugia globulosa	-0.2
3.87	Nebela carinata	Hyalosphenia papilio	14	3.3	Difflugia bacillifera	Arcella discoides	1.7
3.88	Centropyxis aculeata	Pseudodifflugia fulva	15	4.1	Quadrula symmetrica	Phryganella hemisphaerica	3.5
3.89	Nebela griseola	Euglypha cristata[k]	15	4.2	Arcella rotundata var. aplanata[a]	Heleopera sphagni	4.1
3.92	Hyalosphenia elegans	Nebela tubulosa	16	4.8	Arcella discoides	Difflugia leidyi	4.3
3.93	Hyalosphenia papilio	Centropyxis aculeata	16	7.1	Hyalosphenia papilio	Heleopera picta	5.6
4.00	Difflugia leidyi	Hyalosphenia minuta	16	7.8	Nebela marginata	Amphitrema flavum	6.6
4.04	Difflugia bacillariarum	Nebela griseola	17	7.8	Centropyxis aculeata type	Nebela carinata	7.0
4.04	Arcella catinus	Nebela wailesi[j]	18	8.0	Hyalosphenia elegans	Euglypha filifera	8.0
4.12	Euglypha strigosa	Hyalosphenia elegans	18	8.1	Euglypha strigosa[d]	Arcella vulgaris	8.4
4.14	Nebela vitraea	Cyclopyxis arcelloides	20	8.5	Hyalosphenia ovalis	Heleopera petricola	8.4
4.36	Amphitrema flavum	Tracheleuglypha dentata[k]	21	9.1	Heleopera sphagni	Nebela griseola	9.6
4.60	Euglypha ciliata	Arcella gibbosa	21	9.3	Nebela griseola	Hyalosphenia papilio	10.7
4.60	Cyclopyxis arcelloides type	Nebela penardiana[g]	22	10.9	Assulina seminulum	Phryganella acropodia	10.8
4.75	Placocista spinosa	Centropyxis platystoma	22	12.7	Bullinula indica	Hyalosphenia elegans	15.5
4.76	Euglypha tuberculata	Placocista spinosa	24	12.8	Phryganella acropodia	Euglypha ciliata	15.7
4.81	Difflugia pristis type	Euglypha compressa	24	13.0	Sphenoderia lenta	Euglypha strigosa	16.4
5.01	Centropyxis cassis type	Cryptodifflugia oviformis	25	13.5	Arcella catinus	Euglypha laevis	17.3
5.04	Nebela tincta	Bullinularia indica	28	14.1	Corythion dubium type	Euglypha ciliata f. glabra	18.0
5.09	Amphitrema stenostoma	Euglypha ciliata	30	14.6	Euglypha tuberculata	Assulina seminulum	20.4
5.33	Difflugia oblonga	Assulina seminulum	30	15.1	Nebela militaris	Euglypha sp.	20.5
5.46	Nebela marginata			15.1	Nebela parvula	Euglypha anadonta	20.5
5.83	Difflugia rubescens			15.4	Euglypha rotunda	Euglypha compressa f. glabra	21.3
5.99	Difflugia bacillifera			15.6	Arcella artrocrea type	Heleopera petricola c.f.	21.6
6.09	Difflugia penardi			15.8	Heleopera sylvatica	Heleopera petricola var. amethystea	22.1
6.17	Assulina seminulum			16.6	Assulina muscorum	Nebela militaris	22.5
6.52	Nebela parvula			18.6	Centropyxis cassis type	Arcella arenaria	22.8
6.61	Heleopera rosea			19.4	Nebela lageniformis	Placocista lens	23.3
6.79	Assulina muscorum			19.5	Trigonopyxis arcula	Difflugiella oviformis f. fusca	23.7
6.82							

Heleopera sphagni	6.91	Nebela bohemica[o]	40	Cyclopyxis arcelloides-type[r]	20.6	Nebela tincta
Euglypha rotunda	6.95	Heleopera petricola	44	Nebela tincta	22.4	Centropyxis aculeata
Nebela minor	7.09	Nebela dentistoma[l]	48			Assulina muscorum
Corythion-Trinema type	7.14	Nebela militaris	48			Euglypha strigosa f. glabra
Nebela militaris	7.44	Euglypha strigosa	53			Difflugiella oviformis
Nebela flabellulum	7.68	Nebela tincta	58			Nebela parvula
Heleopera petricola	7.87	Corythion dubium[p]	58			Difflugiella apiculata c.f
Trigonopyxis arcula	7.89	Assulina muscorum[p]	59			A. catinus
Hyalosphenia subflava	8.79	Hyalosphenia subflava	59			P. jurassica
Trinema lineare type	9.43	Trigonopyxis arcula	60			Bullinularia indica
Nebela collaris	9.88	Trinema spp.[p]	63			Valkanovia elegans c.f.
Bullinularia indica	10.31	Phryganella acropodia[t]	70			Corythion dubium

24.2	Nebela tincta
24.4	Centropyxis aculeata
24.8	Assulina muscorum
25.1	Euglypha strigosa f. glabra
25.2	Difflugiella oviformis
25.2	Nebela parvula
25.3	Difflugiella apiculata c.f
25.6	A. catinus
25.7	P. jurassica
26.9	Bullinularia indica
27.0	Valkanovia elegans c.f.
28.5	Corythion dubium
28.9	Centropyxis sylvatica
29.2	Trinema lineare var. truncatum
29.5	Trinema lineare
29.7	Centropyxis laevigata
30.6	Trigonopyxis arcula
31.6	Corythion dubium var. orbicularis
32.0	Trinema complanatum
32.4	Corythion pulchellum

Additional notes applicable to table 10 b):

k. There are a number of taxa not fully described in this guide which are reported in other peatland studies and which are not synonymous with any of the other taxa. These include: *Euglypha cristata*, *Tracheleuglypha dentata* and a number of the taxa from Russia (see note t).

l. See *N. wailesi* under *N. lageniformis*. It is likely that these two taxa, which are otherwise similar except in size, have not always been consistently separated in all publications.

m. *Euglypha laevis* separated from *E. rotunda* on the basis of an oval rather than a round mouth.

n. *Arcella arenaria* may be synonymous with *A. catinus*.

o. *Nebela bohemica* may be synonymous with *N. collaris*.

p. The precise division is not known but *Corythion dubium* is probably synonymous with *Corythion-Trinema* type described here and *Trinema* spp. is probably the same as *Trinema lineare*.

q. *Quadrula symmetrica = Quadrulella symmetrica*.

r. *Bullinula indica = Bullinularia indica*.

s. In this case, *Centropyxis cassis* type may also include *Centropyxis platystoma* type.

t. The work of Bobrov *et al.* (1999) used numerous taxonomic divisions which have not been routinely applied in any other peatland ecology studies to test whether more minor taxonomic splitting revealed significant differences between taxa in terms of their ecological niches. This approach is experimental at present. See Bobrov *et al.* (1999) for further details.

taxa as indicators is how to express the data. Taxa such as *A. flavum* can be counted along with pollen but are inevitably expressed as a percentage of a total or partial pollen sum. Although this is convenient, it is not at all logical, since there is no ecological process that connects pollen influx with the living conditions of the testate amoebae. For this reason it is recommended that entire testate amoebae populations from specifically prepared samples are used in all cases unless time and resources are at an extreme premium. Even then, the amount of additional information gained from such analyses may be minimal.

The third possibility is to divide a testate amoebae diagram by wetness zones. Since hydrology is the principal determinant of testate amoebae assemblage, major changes will almost always be explicable in terms of surface wetness changes, especially if nutrient conditions have remained relatively constant. Warner (1990) provides a good example of this in dividing a 10,000 year sequence from a peatland in New Brunswick, Canada into a series of zones reflecting fluctuating hydrological conditions on the mire. In this case, the conditions are again principally inferred from the major taxa – *Hyalosphenia subflava*, *Amphitrema flavum* and *Hyalosphenia papilio*. This approach clearly has advantages in summarising what can be complex data to the non-specialist, as a simple single variable of interest. However, it implies that hydrological changes took place in a series of well-defined phases with sharp transitions between states. This may not be realistic, especially where there are relatively rapid fluctuations in testate amoebae assemblages over a short period of time.

Therefore a fourth method can be used which combines qualitative information on hydrological preferences with the quantitative percentage data for taxa. It thus represents an intermediate approach to the fully quantitative techniques described in the next section. One of the best examples of this approach comes from a study on a Belgian peatland (Beyens, 1985). Here the testate amoebae were divided into the moisture classes I to VIII of Jung (1936) based on Schönborn (1962). The ratio between the 'wet' and 'dry' groups was then used to provide a continuous curve of moisture variability for the profile. This approach is akin to the methods used by Dupont (1986) for reconstructing moisture levels from plant macrofossils and is likely to be a robust approach where reliable data on modern assemblages are not available for the region concerned.

6.3 Quantitative methods

In recent years, there has been a widespread increase in the use of quantitative methods in the interpretation of fossil assemblages of many groups of organisms (Birks, 1995). Studies using testate amoebae have picked up on these methods and application of 'transfer functions' has become a standard approach in more recent work. An excellent full review of these methods is provided by Birks (1995) and we will not go into detail here. The intention of this section is simply to show the basic approach that has been used so far for testate amoebae and to show the kinds of results it produces.

Once modern data on assemblage composition and ecological parameters have been collected, there are three main stages to the application of the transfer function approach. Firstly, the link between assemblage composition and the parameter of interest (depth to water table in most cases) has to be established, usually using ordination techniques. Secondly, the relationship between the modern assemblages and depth to water table needs to be modelled. This may involve testing several models to assess their relative performance. Finally, the regression model (or 'transfer function') is applied to the fossil data and a reconstruction of depth to water table is produced. There are several examples of this approach now published beginning with Warner and Charman (1994) and followed by Woodland *et al.* (1998), and Mitchell *et al.* (1999, 2001). Others have applied existing transfer functions, particularly in the United Kingdom, for example Charman *et al.* (1999) and Charman and Hendon (2000). There is a much greater number of ecological studies that have effectively undertaken the first and sometimes the second of the three steps described above and related assemblage composition to hydrological conditions. These have been reviewed previously in Chapter 2 and section 6.1, above.

The first part of the process in relating assemblages to environmental conditions is normally undertaken by carrying out a correspondence analysis typically using the program CANOCO, which allows the relationship between environmental parameters and taxt to be described. The analysis for the British data collected by Woodland *et al.* (1998) was shown in Chapter 2 (Figure 4). In terms of deriving transfer functions, the main objective of this analysis is to confirm that the variable of interest (e.g. water table) actually shows a strong relationship with the species variability. Once this has been done, the relationship needs to be modelled, using appropriate regression techniques. Until recently this was difficult for most workers who lacked advanced statistical and computational skills. Early work simply applied techniques such as weighted averaging which had been used successfully on other organisms (Warner and Charman, 1994). With the availability of software such as CALIBRATE (Juggins and ter Braak, 1999), the application and testing of a wider range of models has become possible. Typically this will involve testing models based on both unimodal and linear responses of taxa to the environmental parameter, together with several variations on these (Woodland *et al.*, 1998). Different models can be evaluated by comparing water tables (or other variables) predicted by the model with those actually observed at the locations where the modern samples were taken. More reliable comparisons are made if a cross validation approach such as 'jack-knifing' is used where the data used to predict a water table do not include

	Water table depth cm		Moisture content %	
Model	**RMSEP**	**Max. bias**	**RMSEP**	**Max.bias**
WA	3.93	7.13	3.67	8.76
WA-Tol	4.07	7.63	3.44	7.81
WA-PLS	3.93	7.13	3.67	8.78
PLS	4.17	7.13	3.68	8.67

Table 11: A comparison of model performance to predict mean annual water tables and % soil moisture from testate amoebae assemblages in Britain. The RMSEP values represent the 'average' error in predictions of the water table. The maximum bias is a measure of the maximum error of predictions in particular segments of the hydrological gradient. Four models have been tested here. Two are based on weighted averaging (WA and WA-Tol) and one is based on a linear model, partial least squares (PLS) and one is a combination (WA-PLS). In this case the WA and WA-PLS models perform best for reconstructing depth to water table but WA-Tol performs best for reconstructing moisture content. See Woodland *et al.* (1998) for details and further discussion.

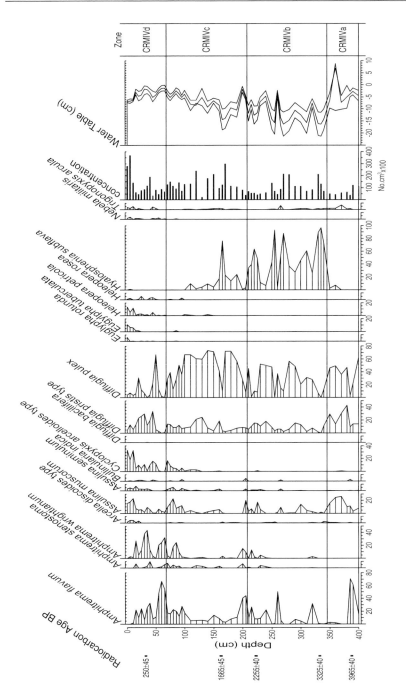

Figure 32: Testate amoebae diagram and reconstructed mean annual water table for a core from Coom Rigg Moss, Northumberland, UK. Here the transfer function of Woodland *et al.* (1998) has been applied to the data set using bootstrapping to provide sample specific error estimates for the water table predictions (from Hendon, 1998; Hendon *et al.*, 2001).

the observed sample for which a prediction is being made (Birks, 1995). Several measures of the adequacy of a model can be used, including the root mean squared error of prediction (RMSEP) and the r^2 value of the predicted and observed values. Table 11 shows the results from an analysis of the British data set discussed by Woodland *et al.* (1998) to illustrate this.

Having derived a suitable transfer function it can then be applied to the fossil data. Often the collection of modern data is done hand-in-hand with the collection of fossil data and exactly the same taxonomic system is applied in both sets of data. However, where this is not the case it is obviously essential that the same taxonomic criteria and nomenclature be applied. Taxonomic harmonisation may be necessary, perhaps grouping some taxa from data sets in which low level splits were made as well as checking consistency in taxa names. Application of the transfer function results in a reconstructed water table curve (Figure 32). sample specific prediction errors can sometimes be estimated by the use of 'bootstrapping' if appropriate software is available (for example Line *et al.*, 1994) which provides a further element of quantification. However, this is normally only possible with estimates based on weighted average approaches. An example of the application of a transfer function is shown in Figure 32.

Summary

The interpretation of fossil testate amoebae data can be carried out in a variety of ways, but it is becoming increasingly obvious that objective, properly quantified estimates of past changes are desirable. There are now a great deal of data which demonstrate the similarities and differences between assemblages from peatlands in different areas of the world. While this increases the likelihood of obtaining reliable reconstructions of hydrology from fossil testate amoebae assemblages, further data are still required from other areas. It will not be possible to provide quantitative estimates of change for all areas, and in these circumstances it is more appropriate to use qualitative and semi-quantitative approaches to reconstruction.

REFERENCES

Aaby, B. 1976. Cyclic variations in climate over the last 5,500 years reflected in raised bogs. *Nature*, 263, 281-284.

Aaby, B., Tauber, H. 1975. Rates of peat formation in relation to degree of humification and local environment as shown by studies of a raised bog in Denmark. *Boreas* 4, 1-17.

Archer, W. 1867. Remarks on freshwater Rhizopoda. *Quarterly Journal of Microscopical Society* 7, 177-179.

Archer, W. 1869. On some freshwater Rhizopoda, new or little known. *Quarterly Journal of Microscopical Society* 9, 321-324.

Archer, W. 1870. On some freshwater Rhizopoda, new or little known. *Quarterly Journal of the Microscopical Society* 10, 17-34 and 101-124.

Archer, W. 1877. Résumé of recent contributions to our knowledge of freshwater Rhizopoda Part IV. *Quarterly Journal of Microscopical Society* 17, 330-353.

Asioli, A., Medioli, F.S., Patterson, R.T. 1996. Thecamoebians as a tool for reconstruction of paleoenvironments in some Italian lakes in the foothills of the Southern Alps (Orta, Varese and Candia). *Journal of Foraminiferal Research*, 26, 248-263.

Awerintzew, S. 1906. Die Süsswasser Rhizopoden. I and II. *Trudui S.-Peterb. Obshch.* 36, 1-351.

Awerintzew, S. 1907. Ueber einige neue Arten gehäusetragender Rhizopoden des Süsswassers *Archiv für Protistenkunde* 8, 86-94.

Barber, K.E. 1981. *Peat stratigraphy and climatic change. A palaeoecological test of the theory of cyclic peat bog regeneration.* Balkema, Rotterdam.

Beyens, L. 1984. A concise survey of testate amoebae analysis. *Bulletin de la Société Belge de Géologie* 93, 261-266.

Beyens, L. 1985. On the subboreal climate of the Belgian Campine as deduced from diatom and testate amoebae analysis. *Review of Palaeobotany and Palynology* 46, 9-31.

Birks, H.J.B. 1995. Quantitative palaeoecological reconstructions. In: Maddy, D. and Brew, J.S. (Eds) *Statistical modelling of Quaternary science data*. Quaternary Research Association, Cambridge, 161-254.

Bobrov, A.A., Charman, D.J., Warner, B.G. 1999. Ecology of testate amoebae (Protozoa:Rhizopoda) on peatlands in western Russia with special attention to niche separation in closely related taxa. *Protist* 150, 125-136.

Bobrov, A.A., Yazvenko, S.B., Warner, B.G. 1995. Taxonomic and ecological implications of shell morphology of three testaceans (Protozoa: Rhizopoda) in Russia and Canada. *Archiv für Protistenkunde* 145, 119-126.

Brown, J.M. 1911. Observations on some new and little known British rhizopods. *Journal of the Linnean Society Zoology* 32, 77-85.

Bütschli, O. 1880. Erster Band. Protozoa. In: Bronn, H.G., *Klassen und Ordnungen des Thier-Reichs*. I Band, I Abth, 1-224.

Buttler, A., Warner, B. G., Grosvernier, P., Matthey, Y. 1996. Vertical patterns of testate amebae (Protozoa:Rhizopoda) and peat-forming vegetation on cutover bogs in the Jura, Switzerland. *New Phytologist,* 134, 371-382.

Carpenter, W.B. 1861. On the systematic arrangement of the Rhizopoda. *Nat. Hist. Rev.* 1861, 456-472.

Carter, H.J. 1864. On freshwater Rhizopoda of England and India. *Annals and Magazine of Natural History series three* 3, 18-39.

Carter, H.J. 1865. On the fresh- and salt-water Rhizopoda of England and India. *Annals and Magazine of Natural History series three* 15, 277-293.

Cash, J. 1891. The freshwater rhizopoda of the Manchester district. *Transactions of the Manchester Microscopic Society* 1891, 47-55.

Cash, J., Hopkinson, J. 1905. *The Freshwater Rhizopoda and Helioza.* Vol. I Rhizopoda part 1. The Ray Society, London, 150 pp.

Cash, J., Hopkinson, J. 1909. *The British Freshwater Rhizopoda and Helioza.* Vol. II Rhizopoda part 2. The Ray Society, London, 166pp.

Cash, J., Wailes, G.H., Hopkinson, J. 1915. *The British Freshwater Rhizopoda and Helioza.* Vol. III Rhizopoda part 3. The Ray Society, London, 156 pp.

Cash, J., Wailes, G.H., Hopkinson, J. 1919. *The British Freshwater Rhizopoda and Helioza.* Vol. IV Supplement to the Rhizopoda. The Ray Society, London, 130 pp.

Chardez, D. 1960. Introduction à l'étude des Thécamoebiens du sol. *Bulletin de l'Institut Agronomique et des Stations de Recherche de Gembloux*, 28(2), 118-131.

Chardez, D. 1964. Thécamoebiens (Rhizopodes testacés). In: Symoens, J-J. (ed.) *Exploration hydrobiologique du bassin du Lac Bangweolo et du Luapula. Résultats scientifiques, Thécamoebiens,* 10(2). Cercle Hydrobiologique de Bruxelles, Brussells, pp.1-77.

Charman, D.J. 1997. Modelling hydrological relationships of testate amoebae (Protozoa: Rhizopoda) on New Zealand peatlands. *Journal of the Royal Society of New Zealand* 27, 465-483.

Charman, D.J., Hendon, D. 2000. Long-term changes in soil water tables over the past 4500 years: relationships with climate and North Atlantic atmospheric circulation and sea surface temperature. *Climatic Change*, in press.

Charman, D.J., Hendon, D., Packman, S. 1999. Multi-proxy surface wetness records from replicate cores on an ombrotrophic mire: implications for Holocene palaeoclimate records. *Journal of Quaternary Science* 14, 451-464.

Charman, D.J., Roe, H.M., Gehrels, W.R. 1998. The use of testate amoebae in studies of sea-level change: a case study from the Taf estuary, South Wales, UK. *The Holocene*, 8, 209-218.

Charman, D.J., Warner, B.G. 1992. Relationship between testate amoebae (Protozoa:Rhizopoda) and microenvironmental parameters on a forested peatland in northeastern Ontario. *Canadian Journal of Zoology*, 70, 2474-2482.

Charman, D.J., Warner, B.G. 1997. The ecology of testate amoebae (Protozoa: Rhizopoda) in oceanic peatlands in Newfoundland, Canada: modelling hydrological relationships for palaeoenvironmental reconstruction. *Écoscience* 4, 555-562.

Claparéde, E., Lachmann, J. 1859. Extrait. *Mémoires de l'Institut National Genevois*, 6 (for *1858)*, 261-482.

Cockerell, T.D.A. 1911. The nomenclature of the Rhizopoda. *Zoologischer Anzeiger* 38, 136-137.

Collins, E.S., McCarthy, F.M., Medioli, F.S., Scott, D.B., Honig, C.A. 1990. Biogeographic distribution of modern thecamoebians in a transect along the eastern North American coast. In: Hemleben, C., Kaminski, M.A., Kuhnt, W., Scott, D.B. (Eds.), *Paleoecology, biostratigraphy, paleocoanography and taxonomy of agglutinated Foraminifera*. NATO Advanced Study Institute Series C Mathematical and Physical Sciences, 327, pp.783-791.

Committee on Systematics and Evolution of the Society of Protozoologists 1980. A newly revised classification of the Protozoa. *Journal of Protozoology* 27, 37-58.

Corbet, S.A. 1973. An illustrated introduction to the testate Rhizopods in *Sphagnum* with special reference to the area around Malham Tarn, Yorkshire. *Field Studies* 3, 801-838.

Costan, G., Planas, D. 1986. Effects of a short-term experimental acidification on a microinvertebrate community: Rhizopoda, Testacea. *Canadian Journal of Zoology* 64, 1224-1230.

De Graaf, F. 1956. Studies on Rotaria and Rhizopoda from the Netherlands. *Biologisch Jaarboek Dodonea* 23, 145–217.

De Saedeleer, H. 1934. Beitrag zur Kenntnis der Rhizopoden: morphologische und systematische Untersuchungen und ein Klassifikationsversuch. *Mémoires du Musèes Royal d'Histoire naturelle de Belgique* 60, 1-128.

Decloitre, L. 1962a. Le genre *Euglypha* Dujardin. *Archiv für Protistenkunde* 106, 53-100.

Decloitre, L. 1962b. Thecamoebiens d'une jouchale naturelle *Internationale Revue Hydrobiologie* 47, 157-163.

Decloitre, L. 1976. Le genre *Arcella* Ehrenberg. Compléments á jour au 31. Décembre 1974 de la monographie du genre parue an 1936. *Archiv für Protistenkunde* 118, 291-309.

Decloitre, L. 1977a. Le genre *Nebela* Compléments á jour au 31. Décembre 1974 de la monographie du genre parue an 1936. *Archiv für Protistenkunde* 119, 325-352.

Decloitre, L. 1977b. The genus *Cyclopyxis*, supplement to the monograph from 1929. *Archiv für Protistenkunde* 119, 34-53.

Decloitre, L. 1978. The genus *Centropyxis* I. supplement to the monograph from 1929. *Archiv für Protistenkunde* 120, 63-85.

Decloitre, L. 1979a. The genus *Centropyxis* II. Supplement to the monograph from 1929. *Archiv für Protistenkunde* 121, 162-192.

Decloitre, L. 1979b. The genera *Arcella, Centropyxis, Euglypha* and *Nebela*. Supplement to the supplements closed 31.12.1974. *Archiv für Protistenkunde* 122, 387-397.

Decloitre, L. 1981. Le genre *Trinema* Dujardin 1841. Révision à jour au 31.12.1979. *Archiv für Protistenkunde* 124, 193-218.

Decloitre, L. 1982. The genera *Arcella, Centropyxis, Cyclopyxis, Euglypha, Nebela* and *Trinema*. Supplements closed 31.12.1981. *Archiv für Protistenkunde* 126, 393-407.

Deflandre, G. 1928. La genre *Arcella* Ehrenburg. Morphologie-Biologie. Essai phylogénétique et systématique. *Archiv für Protistenkunde* 64, 152-287.

Deflandre, G. 1929. Le genre *Centropyxis* Stein. *Archiv für Protistenkunde* 67, 323-375.

Deflandre, G. 1936. Etude monographique sur le genre *Nebela* Leidy (Rhizopoda, Testacea). *Annales für Protistenkunde* 5, 201-322.

Dujardin, F. 1837. Sur une nouvelle espèce de *Gromia* et sur les Difflugies. *Annales des Sciences Naturelles, series two* 8, 310-313.

Dujardin, F. 1841. Histoire naturele des Zoophytes. Infusoires: comprenant la physiologie et la classification de ces animaux, et la manière de les étudier à l'aide du microscope. De Roret, collection 'Nouvelles suite à buBuffon, formant avec les oeuvres de cet auteir, un cours complet d'Histoire naturelle.' Text volume pI-XII and 1-684. Plates volume p.1-14, pls 1-16, 16 bis, 17-22. Paris.

Dupont, L.M. 1986. Temperature and rainfall variation in the Holocene based on comparative palaeoecology and isotope geology of a hummock and a hollow (Boutangerveen, the Netherlands). *Review of Palaeobotany and Palynology*, 48, 71-159.

Dwyer, R.B., Mitchell, F.J.G. 1997. Investigation of the environmental impact of remote volcanic activity on north Mayo, Ireland, during the mid-Holocene. *The Holocene*, 7, 113-118.

Ehrenberg, C.G. 1830. *Organisation, Systematik und geographisches Verhältnis der Infusionsthierchen.* Druckerei der Königlichen Akademie der Wissenschaften, Berlin.

Ehrenberg, C.G. 1832a. Beiträg zur Kenntnis der Organisation der Infusorien und ihrer geographischen Verbreitung, besonders in Sibirien. *Königliche Akademie der Wissenschaften zu Berlin Abhandlungen, 1830, Physikalische Klasse*, 1-88.

Ehrenberg, C.G. 1832b. Über die Entwicklung und Lebensdauer der Infusionsthiere, nebst ferneren Beiträgen zu einer Vergleichung ihrer organischen Systeme. *Königliche Akademie der Wissenschaften zu Berlin Abhandlungen, 1831, Physikalische Abhandlungen*, 1-154.

Ehrenberg, C.G. 1838. *Die Infusionthierchen als vollkommene Organismen. Ein Blick in das tiefere organische Leben der Natur.* L.Voss, Leipzig, pp.1-547.

Ehrenberg, C.G. 1840. Das grössere Infusorienwerke. *Königliche Akademie der Wissenschaften zu Berlin Abhandlungen, 1840, Physikalische Abandlungen*, 198-219.

Ehrenberg, C.G. 1843. Verbreitung und Einfluss des mikroskopischen Lebens in Süd- und Nord-Amerika. *Königliche Akademie der Wissenschaften zu Berlin Abhandlungen, 1841, Physikalische Abandlungen*, 291-446.

Ehrenberg, C.G. 1845. Ueber das kleinste organische Leben an mehreren bisher nicht untersuchten Erdpunkten. *Königliche Akademie der Wissenschaften zu Berlin Abhandlungen, 1845, Physikalische Abandlungen*, 304-321.

Ehrenberg, C.G. 1848. Fortgesetzte Beobachtungen über jetzt herrschende atmosphärische mikroskopische Verhältnisse. *Bericht über die zur Bekanntmachung geeigneten Verhandlungen der Königlichen Preussischen Akademie der Wissenschaften zu Berlin* 13, 370-381.

Ehrenberg, C.G. 1872. Nachtrag zur Übersicht der organischen Atmosphärilen. *Königliche Akademie der Wissenschaften zu Berlin, Physikalische Abhandlungen 1871*, 1-150, 233-275.

Ellison, R.L. 1995. Paleolimnological anlaysis of Ullswater using testate amoebae. *Paleolimnology* 13, 51-63.

Ellison, R.L., Ogden, C.G. 1987. A guide to the study and identification of fossil testate amoebae in Quaternary lake sediments. *International Review of Hydrobiology* 72, 639-652.

Finlay, B.J., Coliss, J.O., Esteban, G., Fenchel, T. 1996. Biodiversity at the microbial level: the number of free-living ciliates in the biosphere. *The Quarterly Review of Biology* 71, 221-237.

Frey, D.G. 1964. Remains of animals in Quaternary lake and bog sediments and their interpretation. *Archiv für Hydrobiologia Beihefte Limnologie* 2 (I-II), 1-114.

Gassowsky, G.N. 1936. Nvye Rhizopoda iz ozer konchezerskoi gruppy (v. karelii). *Trudy Borodinskoi Biologischeskoi Stantsii* 8, 101-121.

Gauthier-Lièvre, L., Thomas, R. 1958. Les genres *Difflugia, Pentagonia, Maghrebia* et *Hoogenraadia* (Rhizopodes testacés) en Afrique. *Archiv für Protistenkunde*, 103, 241-370.

Greef, R. 1866. Ueber einige in der Amöben und andere Rhizopoden. *Archiv für Mikroskopische Anatomie* 2(2-3), 299-331.

Greeff, R. 1888. Studien über Protozoen. *Sitzungsberichte der Gesellschaft zur Beförderung der gesammten Naturwissenschaften zu Marburg*, 3, 90-158.

Grospietsch, Th. 1953. Rhizopodenanalytische Untersuchungen an Mooren Ostholsteins. *Archiv für Hydrobiologie* 47, 321-452.

Grospietsch, Th. 1958. *Wechseltierchen (Rhizopodon). Einführung in die Kleinlebewelt.* Kosmos. Stuttgart.

Grospietsch, Th. 1964. Die Gattungen *Cryptodifflugia* und *Difflugiella* (Rhizopoda, testacea). *Zoologischer Anzeiger* 172, 243-257.

Grospietsch, Th. 1965. Monographische Studie der Gattung *Hyalosphenia* Stein (Rhizopoda, Testacea). *Hydrobiologia* 26, 211-241.

Harnisch, O. 1927. Einigie Daten zur rezenten und fossil testacean Rhizopoden-Fauna der Sphagnen. *Archiv für Hydrobiologie* 18, 246-360

Heal, O.W. 1961. The distribution of testate amoebae (Rhizopoda: testacea) in some fens and bogs in northern England. *Journal of the Linnean Society, Zoology* 44, 369-382.

Heal, O.W. 1962. The abundance and micro-distribution of testate amoebae (Rhizopoda: Testacea) in *Sphagnum. Oikos* 13, 35-47.

Heal, O. 1963. Morphological variation in certain testacea (Protozoa: Rhizopoda). *Archiv für Protistenkunde* 106, 351-368.

Heal, O.W. 1964. Observations on the seasonal and spatial distribution of testacea (Protozoa: Rhizopoda) in Sphagnum. *Journal of Animal Ecology* 33, 395-412.

Hendon, D. 1998. *Robustness and precision of Holocene palaeoclimatic records from peatlands using testate amoebae analysis.* PhD thesis, University of Plymouth, UK.

Hendon, D., Charman, D.J. 1997. The preparation of testate amoebae (Protozoa:Rhizopoda) samples from peat. *The Holocene* 7, 199-205.

Hendon, D., Charman, D.J., Kent, M. 2001. Comparisons of the palaeohydrological record derived from testate amoebae analysis from peatlands in Northern England: within-site variability, between-site comparability and palaeoclimatic implications. *The Holocene 11 (2)*, in press.

Hertwig, R., Lesser, E. 1874. Ueber Rhizopoden und denselben nahestehende Organismen. *Archiv für Mikroskopische Anatomie* 10, 35-243.

Honigberg, B.M., Balamuth, W. 1963. Subphylum Sarcomastigophora nom. nov. to embrace the flagellate and amoeboid assemblages of protozoans. *Journal of Protozoology* 10(suppl.), 27.

Hoogenraad, H.R., de Groot, A.A. 1940. *Zoetwater-rhizopoden en heliozoën. Fauna von Nederland: Aflerering 9.* Leiden, 303pp.

Hoogenraad, H.R., de Groot, A.A. 1948. Thecamoebous Moss-Rhizopods from New Zealand. *Hydrobiologia* 1, 28-44.

Ingram, H.A.P. 1978. Soil layers in mires: function and terminology. *Journal of Soil Science* 29, 224-227.

Juggins, S., ter Braak, C.J.F. 1999. *CALIBRATE version 0.85.* Univeristy of Newcastle Upon Tyne.

Jung, W. 1936. Thekamöben ursprünglicher, lebender deutscher Hochmoore. *Abhandlungen Landesmuseum der Provinz Westfalen Museum für Naturkunde* 7, 1-87.

Kent, S. 1880. *A manual of the Infusoria.* David Bogue, London. 432pp.

Lagerheim, G. 1902. Om lämningar af rhizopoder, heliozoer och tintinnider I Sveriges och Finlands lakustrina kvartäraflagringar. *Geologiska Föreningar Forhandlingar,* 23, 469-520.

Lamarck, J.B. 1816. *Histoire naturelle des animaux sans vertèbres.* Verdière, Paris, vol 2. 1-568.

Leidy, J. 1874. Notice on some Rhizopoda. *Academy of Natural Sciences of Philadelphia Proceedings, series 3, 1874,* 155-157.

Leidy, J. 1875. Remarks on Rhizopods. *Academy of Natural Sciences of Philadelphia Proceedings,* 1875, 413-415.

Leidy, J. 1876a. Remarks on *Arcella. Academy of Natural Sciences of Philadelphia Proceedings,* 1876, 54-58.

Leidy, J. 1876b. Remarks on the rhizopod genus *Nebela. Academy of Natural Sciences of Philadelphia Proceedings,* 1876, 115-119. 18 figs.

Leidy, J. 1878. Species of *Euglypha, Trinema, Pamphagus* and *Cyphoderia. Academy of Natural Sciences of Philadelphia Proceedings,* 1878, 171-173.

Leidy, J. 1879a. *Freshwater Rhizopods of North America.* United States Geological Survey of the Territories no 12. 324pp.

Leidy, J. 1879b. On rhizopods occurring in *Sphagnum. Academy of Natural Sciences of Philadelphia Proceedings,* 1879, 162-163.

Lindberg, H. 1899. En rik torffyndighet I Jorvis-socken Savolaks. *Finska Mosskultur-föreningens Årsbok 1899*, 178-213.

Line, J.M., ter Braak, C.J.F., Birks, H.J.B. 1994. WACALIB version 3.3 - a computer program to reconstruct environmental variables from fossil assemblages by weighted averaging and to derive sample-specific errors of prediction. *Journal of Paleolimnology*, 10, 147-152.

Loeblich, A.R.Jr., Tappan, H. 1964. Sarcodina, chiefly "Thecamoebians" and Foraminiferida. In: Moore, R. C. (Ed.), *Treatise on Invertebrate Paleontology: Part C, Protista 2(1)*. Geological Society of America and University of Kansas Press, 510pp.

Lousier, J.D. 1984a. Population dynamics and production studies of *Phryganella acropodia* and *Difflugia oviformis* (Testacea, Rhizopoda, Protozoa) in an aspen wood-land soil. *Pedobiologia* 1, 268-278.

Lousier, J.D. 1984b. Population dynamics and production studies of species of Euglyphidae (Testacea, Rhizopoda, Protozoa). *Archiv für Protistenkunde* 136, 153-189.

Lousier, J.D., Parkinson, D. 1981. The disappearance of empty tests of litter and soil testate amoebae (Testacea, Rhizopoda, Protozoa). *Archiv für Protistenkunde* 124, 312-336.

Lüftenegger, G., Petz, W., Berger, H., Foissner, W., Adam, H. 1988. Morphological and biometric characterization of twenty-four soil testate amoebae. *Archiv für Protistenkunde* 136, 153-189.

Mauquoy, D., Barber, K. 1999. Evidence for climatic deteriorations associated with the decline of *Sphagnum imbricatum* Hornsch ex. Russ. in six ombrotrophic mires from northern England and the Scottish Borders. *The Holocene*, 9, 423-437.

McCarthy, F.M.G., Collins, E.S., McAndrews, J.H., Kerr, H.A., Scott, D.B., Medioli, F.S. 1995. A comparison of postglacial Arcellacean ('Thecamoebian') and pollen suc-cession in Atlantic Canada, illustrating the potential of Arcellaceans for palaeoclimatic reconstruction. *Journal of Paleontology* 69, 980-993.

McGlone, M.S., Wilmshurst, J.M. 1999. A Holocene record of climate, vegetation change and peat bog development, east Otago, South Island, New Zealand. *Journal of Quater-nary Science*, 14, 239-254.

Medioli, F.S. Scott, D.B. 1983. *Holocene Arcellacea (Thecamoebians) from eastern Canada.* Cushman Foundation, Washington D.C.

Medioli, F.S., Scott, D.B. 1988. Lacustrine thecamoebians (mainly Arcellaceans) as potential tools for palaeolimnological interpretations. *Paleogeography, Paleoeclimatology, Paleoecology,* 62, 361-386.

Medioli, F.S., Scott, D.B., Abbott, B.H. 1987. A case study of protozoan intraclonal variability: taxonomic implications. *Journal of Foraminiferal Research* 17, 28-47.

Medioli, F.S., Scott D.B., McCarthy, F.M.G., 1990. Fossil thecamoebians: present status and prospects for the future. In: Hemleben *et al.*, (Eds.) NATO ASI Series C. 327, pp. 813-840.

Meisterfeld, R. 1977. Die horizontale und vertikale Verteilung der Testaceen (Rhizopoden, Testacea) in *Sphagnum. Archiv für Hydrobiologie* 79, 319-356.

Meisterfeld, R. 1979. Contribution to the systematik of testacea (Rhizopoda, Testacea) in *Sphagnum* A SEM investigation. *Archiv für Protistenkunde* 121, 246-269.

Mignot, J.P., Raikov, I.B. 1992. Evidence for meiosis in the testate amoeba *Arcella. Journal of Protozoology* 39, 287-289.

Mitchell, E.A.D., Buttler, A.J., Warner, B.G., Gobat, J.-M. 1999. Ecology of testate amoebae (Protozoa: Rhizopoda) in *Sphagnum* peatlands in the Jura mountains, Switzerland and France. *Écoscience* 6, 565-576.

Mitchell, E.A.D., van der Knaap, W.O., van Leeuwen, J.F.N., Buttler, A.J., Warner, B.G., Gobat, J.-M. 2001. The palaeoecological history of the Praz-Rodet bog (Swiss Jura) based on pollen, plant macrofossils and testate amoebae (Protozoa). *The Holocene* 11, in press.

Moore, P.D., Webb, J.A., Collinson, M.E. 1991. *Pollen analysis.* Blackwell, Oxford.

Nüsslin, O. 1884 Ueber einige neue Urthiere aus dem Herrenwieser See im badischen Schwarzwalde. *Zeitschrift für Wissenschaften Zoologie* 15, 697-724.

Ogden, C.G. 1980. Shell structure in some pyriform species of *Difflugia* (Rhizopodea). *Archiv für Protistenkunde* 123, 455-470.

Ogden, C.G. 1981. Observations on clonal cultures of Euglyphidae (Rhizopoda, Protozoa). *Bulletin of the British Museum (Natural History)* 41, 137-151.

Ogden, C.G. 1983. Observations on the systematics of the genus *Difflugia* in Britain (Rhizopoda, Protozoa). *Bulletin of the British Museum (Natural History) Zoology Series* 44, 1-73.

Ogden, C.G. 1984. Shell structure of some testate amoebae from Britain. *Journal of Natural History* 18, 341-361.

Ogden, C.G., Hedley, R.H. 1980. *An atlas of freshwater testate amoebae.* British Museum (Natural History), Open University Press, Oxford.

Page, F.C. 1966. *Cryptodifflugia operculata* n. sp. (Rhizopodea:Arcellinida, Cryptodifflugiidae) and the status of the Genus *Cryptodifflugia. Transactions of the American Microscopical Society* 85, 506-515.

Patterson, D.J., Hedley, S. 1992. *Free-living freshwater Protozoa.* Wolfe Publishing, London, 223pp.

Patterson, R.T. 1987. Arcellaceans and foraminifera from Pleistocene Lake Tecopa, California. *Journal of Foraminiferal Research,* 17, 333-343.

Patterson, R.T., Barker, T., Burbidge, S.M. 1996. Arcellaceans (Thecamoebians) as proxies of arsenic and mercury contamination in northeastern Ontario Lakes. *Journal of Foraminiferal Research,* 26, 172-183.

Patterson, T., Kumar, A. 2000. Use of Arcellacea (Thecamoebians) to gauge levels of contamination and remediation in industrially polluted lakes. In: Martin, R. (Ed.) *Environmental Micropaleontology.* Kluwer, in press.

Patterson, R.T., Mackinnon, K.D., Scott, D.B., Medioli, F.S. 1985. Arcellaceans ('thecamoebians') in small lakes of New Brunswick and Nova Scotia: modern distribution and Holocene stratigraphic changes. *Journal of Foraminiferal Research* 15, 114-137.

Penard, E. 1890. Étude sur les Rhizopodes d'eau douce. *Mémoires de la Société de Phy-*

sique et d'Histoire Naturelle de Genève 31(2), 1-230.

Penard, E. 1891. Rocky Mountain rhizopods. *American Naturalist* 25, 1070-1083.

Penard, E. 1893. *Pelomyxa palustris* et quelques autres organismes inférieurs. *Bibliothèques Universelle, Archives des Sciences Physiques et Naturelles, series 3*, 29(2), 165-182.

Penard, E. 1899. Les Rhizopodes de la faune profonde dans le lac Léman. *Revue Suisse de Zoologie* 7(1), 1-142.

Penard, E. 1901. Notes complémentaires sur les Rhizopodes du Léman. *Revue Suisse de Zoologie* 9, 225-241.

Penard, E. 1902. *Faune Rhizopodique du Bassin du Léman*. Henry Kündig, Genève. 714pp.

Penard, E. 1905. Notes sur quelques Sarcodinès. *Revue Suisse de Zoologie* 13(3), 585-616, pls13-14.

Penard, E. 1907. On some rhizopods from the Sikkim Himalaya. *Journal of the Royal Microscopical Society* 1907, 274-278.

Penard, E. 1911. Rhizopodes d'eau douce. In: Murray, J. (Ed.), *British Antarctic Expedition 1907-1909, under the command of Sir E.H. Shackleton CVO. Reports on the scientific investigations vol 1, Biology Part 6*, pp.203-262.

Penard, E. 1912. Notes sur quelques Sarcodinés. *Revue Suisse de Zoologie* 20(1), 1-29.

Perty, M. 1849a. Über vertikale Verbreitung mikroskopischer Lebensformen. *Naturforschende Gesellschaft in Bern Mittheilungen 1849*, 17-49

Perty, M. 1849b. Mikroskopische Organismen der Alpen und der italienischen Schweiz. *Naturforschende Gesellschaft in Bern Mittheilungen 1849*, 153-176.

Perty, M. 1852. *Zur Kenntnis kleinster Lebensformen nach Bau, Funktionen, Systematik, mit Spezialverzeichnis der in der Schweiz beobachteten*. Jent and Reinert, Bern, 228pp.

Playfair, G.I. 1917. Rhizopods of Sydney and Lismore. *Proceedings of the Linnean Society of New South Wales* 42, 633-675.

Reinhardt, E.G., Dalby, A., Kumar, A., Patterson, R.T. 1998. Utility of Arcellacean morphotypic variants as pollution indicators in mine tailing contaminated lakes near Cobalt, Ontario, Canada. *Micropaleontology*, 44, 131-148.

Rhumbler, L. 1895. Beiträge zur Kenntnis der Rhizopoden. (Beiträg III, IV und V). *Zeitschrift für Wissenschaften Zoologie* 61(1), 38-110.

Ruzicka, E. 1982. Die subfossilen Testaceen des Krottensees (Salzburg, Österreich). *Limnologica* 1, 231-254.

Schlumberger, P. 1845. Observations sur quelques nouvelles espèces d'Infusoires de la famille des Rhizopodes. *Annales des Sciences Naturelles, Zoologie, series three* 3, 254-256.

Schmarda, L.C. 1871. *Zoologie. Vol. 1.* Braumüller, Vienna.

Schönborn, W. 1962. Zur Ökologie der sphagnikolen, bryokolen un terrikolen Testaceen. *Limnologica* 1, 231-254.

Schönborn, W. 1973. Paläolimnologische Studien an Testaceen des Latnjajaure (Abisko-Gebiet, Swedisch Lappland). *Hydrobiologia*, 42, 63-75.

Schönborn, W. 1984. Studies on remains of testacea in cores of the Great Woryty Lake (NE-Poland). *Limnologica* 16, 185-190.

Schönborn, W. 1992a. Adaptive polymorphism in soil-inhabiting testate amebas (Rhizopoda) - its importance for delimitation and evolution of asexual species. *Archiv für Protistenkunde* 142, 139-155.

Schönborn, W. 1992b. Comparative studies on the production biology of protozoan communities in freshwater and soil ecosystems. *Archiv für Protistenkunde* 141, 187-214.

Schönborn, W., Peschke, T. 1988. Biometric studies on species, races, ecophenotypes and individual variations of soil inhabiting Testacea (Protozoa:Rhizopoda), including *Trigonopyxis minuta* n.sp. and *Corythion asperulum* n.sp. *Archiv für Proistenkunde* 136, 345-363.

Schönborn, W., Peschke, T. 1990. Evolutionary studies on the *Assulina-Valkanovia* complex (Rhizopoda, Testaceafiliosia) in *Sphagnum* and soil. *Biology and Fertility of Soils*

9, 95-100.

Schulze, F.E. 1875. Rhizopodenstudien. IV. *Archiv für Mikroskopische Anatomie* 11, 329-353.

Scott, D.B., Medioli, F.S. 1983. Agglutinated rhizopods in Lake Erie: modern distribution and stratigraphic implications. *Journal of Paleontology* 57, 809-820.

Sleigh, M.A. 1989. *Protozoa and other protists.* 4th edition, Edward Arnold, London.

Steinecke, F. 1927. Leitformen und Leitfossilien des Zehlaubruches: die Bedeutung der fossilen Mikro-organismen für Erkenntniss der Nekrozonosen eines Moores. *Botanische Archiv: zeitschrift für die gesamte Botanik (Koenigsberg)* 19, 327-344.

Stockmarr, J. 1971. Tablets with spores used in absolute pollen analysis. *Pollen et Spores* 13, 615-621.

Taranek, K.J. 1881. Beiträge zur Kenntniss der Süsswasser- Rhizopoden Böhmens. *Sitzungsbericht Böhmischer Gesellschaften Wissenschaften* 1881, 220-235.

Taranek, K.J. 1882. Monographie der Nebeliden Böhmen's. Ein Beitrag zur Kenntniss der Süsswasser Monothalamien. *Abhandlungen der königlichen Böhmischen Gesellschaft der Wissenschaften* 6(11), 1-56.

Thomas, R., Chardez, D. 1958. Étude critique de *Trinema penardi* nom. nov. (Thécamoebie, s). *Cahiers des Naturalistes* 14, 101-104.

Tolonen, K. 1966. Stratigraphic and rhizopod analyses on an old raised bog, Varrassuo, in Hollola, south Finland. *Annales Botanici Fennici* 3, 147-166.

Tolonen, K. 1986. Rhizopod analysis. In: Berglund, B.E. (Ed.), *Handbook of Holocene palaeoecology and palaeohydrology.* John Wiley, Chichester, pp.645-666.

Tolonen, K., Huttunen, P., Jungner, H. 1985. Regeneration of two coastal raised bogs in eastern North America. *Annales Academiae Scientiarum Fennicae Series A,* 139, 5-51.

Tolonen, K., Warner, B. G., Vasander, H. 1992. Ecology of testaceans (Protozoa: Rhizopoda) in mires in southern Finland: I. Autecology. *Archiv für Protistenkunde,* 142, 119-138.

Tolonen, K., Warner, B. G., Vasander, H. 1994. Ecology of testaceans (Protozoa: Rhizopoda) in mires in southern Finland: II. Multivariate analysis. *Archiv für Protistenkunde*, 144, 97-112.

Van der Molen, P.C., Hoekstra, S.P. 1988. A palaeoecological study of the hummock-hollow complex from Engbertsdijksveen, in the Netherlands. *Review of Palaeobotany and Palynology* 56, 213-274.

Van der Molen, P.C., Van't Veer, R., Wijmstra, T.A. 1992. Palaeo-ecology of hummock-hollow complexes on raised bogs in the Irish Midlands. In: Van der Molen, P.C., *Hummock-hollow complexes on Irish raised bogs. a Palaeo/Actuo ecological approach of environmental and climatic change.* Academisch Proefschrift, University of Amsterdam, pp.83-113.

Van Geel, B. 1978. A palaeoecological study of Holocene peat bog sections in Germany and the Netherlands, based on the analysis of pollen, spores and macro- and microscopic remians of fungi, algae, cormophytes and animals. *Review of Palaeobotany and Palynology* 25, 1-120.

Van Oye, P. 1956. On the thecamoeban fauna of New Zealand with description of four new species and biogeographical discussion. *Hydrobiologia* 8, 16-37

Von Siebold, C.T.E. 1845. Bericht über die Leistungen in der Naturgeschichte der Würmer, Zoophyten Protozoen während des Jahres 1843 und 1844. *Archiv für Naturgeschichte* 11, 256-296.

Von Stein, S.F.N. 1857. Die wirbellosen Thiere. *Icones Zootomicae.* J.V. Carus, Leipzig.

Von Stein, S.F.N. 1859. Über die ihm aus eigener Untersuchung bekannt gewordenen Süsswasser-Rhizopoden. *Königliche Böhmische Gesellschaft der Wissenschaften Abhandlungen, series 5* 10, 41-43.

Wailes, G.H. 1912a. Freshwater Rhizopoda and Heliozoa from the states of New York, New Jersey and Georgia, USA, with supplemental note on Seychelles species. *Journal of the Linnean Society (Zoology)* 32, 121-161.

Wailes, G.H. 1912b. Freshwater Rhizopoda from the Hebrides, Orkney and Shetland Islands and Western Scotland, with description of a new species. *Scottish Naturalist* 141,

59-65.

Wailes, G.H. 1913. Freshwater Rhizopods from North and South America. *Journal of the Linnean Society (Zoology)* 32, 201-218.

Wailes, G.H., Penard, E. 1911. Clare Island Survey: Rhizopoda. *Proceedings of the Royal Irish Academy* 31(65), 1-64.

Wallich, G.C. 1863. Further observations on the distinctive characters, habits and reproductive phenomena. *Annals and Magazine of Natural History, series three,* 12, 448-468.

Wallich, G.C. 1864. On the extent and some of the principal causes of structural variation among the Difflugian rhizopods *Annals and Magazine of Natural History, series three* 13, 215-245.

Wanner, M., Meisterfeld, R. 1994. Effects of some environmental factors on the shell morphology of testate amoebas (Rhizopoda, Protozoa). *European Journal of Protistology*, 30, 191-195.

Warner, B.G. 1987. Abundance and diversity of testate amoebae (Rhizopoda, Testacea) in *Sphagnum* peatlands in southwestern Ontario, Canada. *Archiv für Protistenkunde*, 133, 173-189.

Warner, B.G. 1989. Fossil testate amoebae (Protozoa) and hydrological history of an obrotrophic bog in northwestern Ontario, Canada. *Proceedings of the international symposium on peat/peatland characteristics and uses.* Spigarelli, S.A. (Ed.). Bemidji State University, Bemidji, Minnestoa, pp5-14.

Warner, B.G. 1990. Testate amoebae (Protozoa). Methods in Quaternary ecology no. 5. *Geoscience Canada* 5, 65-74.

Warner, B.G., Charman, D.J. 1994. Holocene soil moisture changes on a peatland in northwestern Ontario based on fossil testate amoebae (Protozoa) analysis. *Boreas*, 23, 270-279.

Wilmshurst, J. 1998. And in the bog there lived... *New Zealand Science Monthly* 9, 9-10.

Woodland, W.A. 1996. *Holocene palaeohydrology from testate amoebae: developing a model for British peatlands.* PhD thesis, University of Plymouth, UK.

Woodland, W.A., Charman, D.J., Sims, P.C. 1998. Quantitative estimates of water tables and soil moisture in Holocene peatlands from testate amoebae. *The Holocene* 8, 261-273.

ALPHABETICAL INDEX TO TAXA